THE TECHNICAL DEVELOPMENT OF ROADS IN BRITAIN

The Technical Development of Roads in Britain

GRAHAM WEST

Ashgate

Aldershot • Burlington USA • Singapore • Sydney

Published by
Ashgate Publishing Ltd
Gower House
Croft Road
Aldershot
Hants GU11 3HR
England

Ashgate Publishing Company
131 Main Street
Burlington
Vermont 05401
USA

Ashgate website: http://www.ashgate.com

British Library Cataloguing in Publication Data
West, Graham
    The technical development of roads in Britain
    1.Roads - Great Britain - History 2.Roads - Great Britain -
    Design and construction - History 3.Highway engineering -
    Great Britain - History
    I.Title
    625.7'0941

Library of Congress Control Number: 00-134024

ISBN 0 7546 1406 9

Printed in Great Britain by
Antony Rowe Ltd, Chippenham, Wiltshire

Contents

List of Figures

Figure Acknowledgements

Figures 1.1 and 1.2: British Standards Institution.

Figures 1.5, 1.7, 7.3 and 7.4: Transport Research Laboratory.

Figure 2.1: *The Observer*.

Figure 3.4 and 7.7: adapted from C.A. O'Flaherty, *Highways*.

Figures 4.2 and 7.6: adapted from H. Law and D.K. Clark, *The Construction of Roads and Streets*.

Figures 5.1 and 5.2: W. Taylor, *The Military Roads in Scotland*.

Figure 6.4: *The Oxford Illustrated History of Britain*.

Figure 8.2: *Autocar*.

Figures 8.4 and 8.5: adapted from *Highways and Transportation*.

Figure 8.6: Collins.

Figure 9.1: adapted from G.D. Matheson, 'Aspects of Highway Rock Engineering in the UK', Geological Society.

Figure 9.2: *Atlas de la Revolution Français*, Editions EHESS, Paris.

Figures 9.3 and A3.1: British Cement Association.

Figure 9.4: *Sustainability Counts*, Department of the Environment, Transport and the Regions.

Figure 9.5: *Britain 1998*. HM Stationery Office.

List of Tables

Preface

The road is one of the earliest artefacts; moreover it is one that has remained useful to man over almost the whole span of history, although, as we shall see, the road has been more highly prized at some times than at others. As the great Victorian historian Macaulay remarked in his famous aphorism, the road, because it abridges distance, is one of the three great agents of civilisation (the other two, he said, were the alphabet and the printing press). The purpose of this book is to describe and discuss the development of roads in Great Britain with special emphasis on the technical aspects of their construction and use. There are two reasons for this: firstly, the fact that the technical history of roads is interesting in its own right, and secondly, that it is only by considering these technical considerations along with political, social, military and economic matters that we can properly understand the role that the road has played in the history of our country. This is to assert, of course, that technical history becomes much more meaningful if it is integrated with the history of the country as a whole, and *vice versa*.

The author has spent his professional life on the staff of the Transport Research Laboratory, and when embarking on a career of road research in the mid-1950s, an important consideration in this decision was the widely held belief that roads were an unalloyed benefit to mankind. Today no-one could have this simple assurance. The rise of motorway objection groups, and protesters against plans for bypasses and other road improvements, show that the advantage to the many can sometimes only be bought at the expense of a disadvantage to the few. And roads themselves, these days, with their problems of traffic congestion, noise and pollution, and their toll of accidents are now viewed as a mixed blessing.

The three elements of historical writing are description, narrative and analysis. The first two are mainly matters of fact but the third is essentially based on an interpretation of the facts by the historian. In this book the description and narrative follow those of the established authorities on the various aspects of the technical history of roads. However, the interpretation and analysis of these factual matters is primarily that of the author. The subject matter has been collected from a wide range of sources, the more important of which are listed in the Bibliography, and to which grateful acknowledgement is made.

The book explores the technical history of roads in Great Britain primarily by means of an examination of the development of the construction of the *road pavement*, by which is meant the structure of the road, and which is probably its most important characteristic. The matters of geotechnics, embankments, cuttings, retaining walls, bridges and tunnels, and other aspects of modern road construction such as alignment, skidding resistance, riding quality, traffic planning and road layout are not dealt with, not because they are not important, but in order to confine the scope of the book to a manageable size. The study of the need for roads and the consequent development of the road network in Great Britain is a secondary theme of the book. Although the work is concerned with British roads, some descriptions of roads in other parts of Europe are made from time to time where these shed light on developments in Great Britain.

Following an introductory chapter which deals with such matters as terminology and units, and introduces some concepts necessary for an understanding of the rest of the book, chapter 2 describes what might be called the prehistory of roads – in particular the ancient trackways, parts of which can still be seen today. The Romans are regarded as the road builders *par excellence*, and chapter 3 deals with their technical achievements. With the departure of the Romans, roads were then more or less abandoned at a national level for a very long period and chapter 4 describes this age of neglect. The rebirth of roadmaking took place at first in the highlands of Scotland, for military purposes, and this is the subject of chapter 5. The longest chapter in the book is chapter 6 which describes the flowering of roadmaking in the eighteenth and nineteenth century – what might be called the golden age of the road. This period is much loved by historians of technology and transport because of the wealth of material still available for study and because of the romantic appeal of the coaching days. Chapters 7 and 8 bring us into the twentieth century, the former chapter dealing with the coming of the motor car and the bituminously surfaced road, and the latter chapter with the building of motorways. The final chapter of the book draws some general conclusions from the work and makes some pertinent observations. Four Appendices provide further information on rocks, soils, bituminous and concrete materials, and skidding resistance.

The book has been written to be intelligible to the layman, and it has, therefore, been necessary to simplify some technical descriptions and to offer much simplified presentations of what are sometimes complex matters – for example, pavement design, traffic loading and slope stability. However, it is hoped that any highway engineer reading the book will not find the treatment is simplistic. Also, it should be pointed out that the figures used to illustrate the work are, for the most part, diagrammatic and intended mainly to help an understanding of the text. Where they have been borrowed, or adapted, from elsewhere this is gratefully acknowledged at the front of the book.

By a happy coincidence, the history of paved roads in Great Britain approximately corresponds with the Christian calendar, so that the celebration of the start of the third millennium of the one is also the celebration of the start of the third millennium of the other. The publication of this book is, therefore, timely.

The book shows that roads have been a main part of our built environment for some 2,000 years, and are now an essential element of the country's infrastructure. It is the author's belief that the technical history of roads is as much worthy of study as the history of other more impressive branches of civil engineering such as bridges, dams, harbour works, railways and tunnels, particularly if studied in a broad context. If this book has gone some way to introduce roads and the achievements of roadmakers down through the ages to a wider public, it will have achieved one of its objectives.

1 Introduction

Begin at the beginning,
the King said gravely, ...

The history of roads in Great Britain has not been one of steady development, but rather, one that has waxed and waned in response to social, military and economic needs, and also as to whether there have been alternative methods of transport available. Paralleling this, the technical aspects of road construction – with the one great exception of Roman roads – can be seen as a fitful progression of improvement followed by neglect as the roadmaker has responded, albeit tardily on occasion, to the needs of the road user. This book describes the technical development of British roads in relation to the needs of the time, and thereby touches upon its relation to the history of the country more generally.

Terminology and Units

In a book dealing with road construction, some use of the specialised terminology of highway engineering is unavoidable. It is hoped that many of the terms will be understood from their context, but for the general reader a Glossary of technical terms is given at the end of the book. One term especially is liable to be a source of much confusion and must be dealt with straight away: the word 'pavement'. The highway engineer uses the term pavement to mean the whole of the constructed part of the road structure. What the layman calls the pavement is referred to by the highway engineer as the 'footway' in Great Britain, and as the 'sidewalk' in the United States. In this book pavement is used in the highway engineering sense (see Figures 1.1 and 1.2).

The word 'road' comes from the Old English *ridan* meaning to ride, but before 1596 was not used in the sense that we use it today. Before that date, road meant a stretch of water where ships could safely ride at anchor and it is still used in this sense by mariners (e.g. Cowes Roads), but the word used for what we call a road was 'way'. After 1596 road was used with its present-day

1

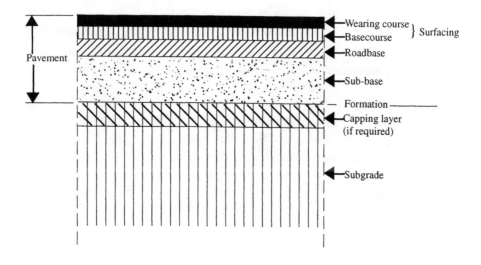

**Figure 1.1   Terms used to describe various layers of construction in a
road with a flexible (bituminous) pavement**

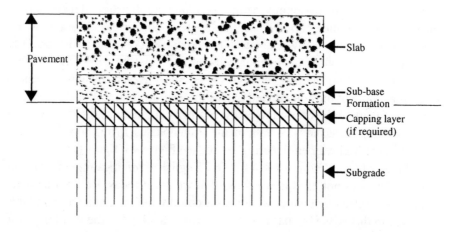

**Figure 1.2   Terms used to describe various layers of construction in a
road with a rigid (concrete) pavement**

meaning and way fell out of use, except that it is still preserved in such terms as highway, footway and right-of-way. Turning to its recent meaning, Section 192 of the Road Traffic Act 1988 defines a road as any way used for the passage of vehicles and further provides: 'Road means any highway and any other road to which the public have access', but in a later ruling, unrestricted pedestrian use (with or without vehicular use) was deemed sufficient for a route to qualify as a road. The proper function of a road was to enable movement along it to a destination.

Ever since their beginning, roads have been used for three main purposes, the transit of people, post and goods, and this is still true today. If soldiers and their equipment come into the categories of people and goods, this also includes the military use of roads. In the past animals, either as beasts of burden or as livestock, were important constituents of road traffic, but now form an insignificant proportion; at one time they were also important for drawing coaches and wagons. In modern times the motor vehicle has come to dominate road traffic and is practically the only consideration of the present-day road designer.

Roads in Great Britain are numbered according to the following method. For this purpose the country is divided into six sections by the six main routes radiating clockwise from London: these are the A1 to Edinburgh, the A2 to Dover, the A3 to Portsmouth, the A4 to Bath, the A5 to Holyhead and the A6 to Carlisle. This can be remembered by the mnemonic: **E**very **D**ay **P**lease o**B**ey the **H**ighway **C**ode. Within each section the first figure of the road number, whether it be a class A, B or C road, is the same as the number of the section. Thus, for example, the A31 and the B3016 lie in the section between the A3 and the A4. When the motorways came to be built, their numbering followed on similar lines starting with the M1 from London to Birmingham.

In January 1969 the construction industry in Great Britain changed from the Imperial system of units to the metric system. This poses a problem for the writer of the history of technology for which there is no simple solution. In this book, in general, for the period before the changeover Imperial units are used and for the subsequent period metric units are used. For the purpose of simple mental comparison of the two, the following approximate conversion factors may be used:

Length
1 mile = 1.6 km
1 yd = 0.9 m
1 ft = 0.3 m
1 in = 25 mm

Force
1 tonf = 10 kN = 1 tonnef
1 lbf = 4.5 N

Pressure
1 lbf/ft^2 = 100 kN/m^2

Capacity
1 lbf/in^2 = 7 kN/m^2

1 gallon = 4.5 litre
1 pint = 0.6 litre

Power
1 hp = 750 W

Mass
1 ton = 1000 kg (1 tonne)   *Temperature*
1 cwt = 50 kg   n °F = 5/9 (n-32) °C
1 lb = 0.5 kg
1 oz = 30g

These conversion factors are not exact and should not be used for any other purpose. The letter f in some of the above units denotes force, thereby distinguishing between units of force (e.g. lbf and tonnef) and the similarly named units of mass (e.g. lb and tonne). Wherever possible, in line with present-day practice, the term 'weight' has been avoided in the book, but for reasons of convention this has not always been done (*weight* being the gravitational force acting on the mass of a body).

The Need for a Pavement

As we shall see, the first roads – those carrying men travelling on foot or on horseback, or those carrying pack animals and occasional herds of domestic animals – did not have a road pavement. But as soon as vehicles of any kind came to be used, a pavement was needed. It is clear that a flat, hard and durable surface is required to allow the vehicle's wheels to run smoothly, but it is not immediately apparent why a thickness of pavement construction is needed. To explain why this is so we shall take a nineteenth-century four-horse stage coach as an example.

A typical vehicle of this kind would have had a mass of 18 cwt and would have carried a load, consisting of passengers and goods, having a mass of 2 tons, giving a gross mass of 6,496 lb, so that the force exerted by each wheel on the surface would have been 1,624 lbf, assuming the weight to be uniformly distributed on all four wheels. The iron tyres of the wheels were 2 in wide, and assuming each tyre was in contact with the surface over a 2 in length of its circumference, this gives a contact area of 4 in^2 per wheel. Each wheel, therefore, exerts a pressure of 406 lbf/in^2 on the surface. The bearing capacities of some typical soil types are:

Gravel: 87 lbf/in^2;
Sand: 44 lbf/in^2; and
Clay: 22 lbf/in^2.

It can be seen that the pressure exerted by each wheel is very considerably greater than all these values, so that the wheels would sink into the surface if the coach tried to run on any of these soils. However, if a layer of well-compacted crushed stone is placed on the soil as a pavement, say 8 in thick, then the load exerted by the wheel will be spread as shown in Figure 1.3. The crushed stone not only has an adequate bearing capacity itself (typically 1000 lbf/in^2), but it also performs the important function of spreading the load so that it can be supported by the soil below. Referring again to Figure 1.3, by assuming a 27° spread, it can be seen that the wheel load of 1624 lbf is now distributed over an area of 10 in x 10 in, so that the pressure on the soil is reduced to 16 lbf/in^2. This is less than the bearing capacity of even the weakest soil. The pavement has therefore provided the means whereby the soil is now capable of supporting the coach.

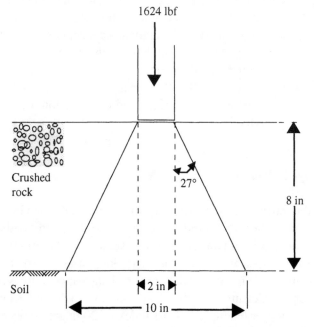

Figure 1.3 Load-spreading function of road pavement

Roadmaking Material

Much of the content of the book is concerned with the material used in road pavement construction, and a word is therefore necessary about its availability in Great Britain. Throughout the whole period being considered – indeed right up to the present day – the overwhelmingly predominant roadmaking material is stone. However, hard rocks are by no means uniformly distributed across the country, and as we shall see, this has affected road construction in different parts. Figure 1.4 shows that Great Britain can be very broadly divided into two basic regions, one to the north and west where hard rocks are plentiful and another to the southeast where only soft rocks and soils are available. Alluvial or glacial gravels and sands occur in all regions but assume much more importance for road construction in the southeast where hard rocks are absent. The main rocks used as roadstones in the United Kingdom are described in more detail in Appendix 1.

The special roadmaking materials used in the twentieth century – various bituminous materials and concrete – are described in chapter 7, but even with these it should be noted that stone in the form of aggregate is predominantly the main constituent, whether it be crushed rock or gravel and sand.

The highway engineer regards *soil* as any naturally occurring loose or soft material that can be excavated with a bulldozer. This definition is, therefore, more wide-ranging than the layman's concept of soil as the surface material that supports vegetation – which the highway engineer calls *topsoil*. The soil directly beneath the road pavement is referred to as the *subgrade*, the prepared surface of which is called the *formation* (see Figures 1.1 and 1.2). The main soil types encountered during road construction are described in more detail in Appendix 2.

Frost Damage to Roads

Apart from the traffic, the greatest enemy of the roadmaker in Great Britain is frost. In the days before bound materials were used in roads this was particularly true, but it remains so to some extent up to the present time. The severity of frost is measured by a parameter known as the frost index. The *frost index* is simply the number of days on which the temperature is continually below zero degrees Celsius multiplied by the number of degrees Celsius below zero on each day. For example, a frost index of 20 degree days could have arisen from 5 days at -2°C followed by 10 days at -1°C, $((5 \times 2) + (10 \times 1) =$

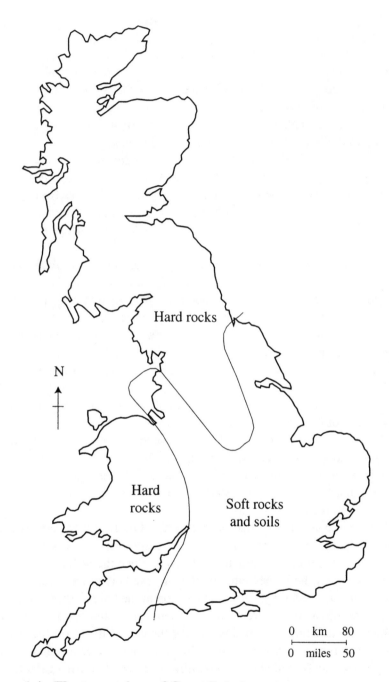

Figure 1.4   The two regions of Great Britain

20). The yearly frost index is the sum of the frost indices for a particular site for a single year, and the mean yearly frost index is the mean value of the yearly frost index for a particular site calculated from data extending over a number of years. The frost index is a measure of the severity of a single cold spell whilst the yearly frost index is a measure of the severity of a single year. The mean yearly frost index is a measure of the average severity of yearly frost at a site, and can be used to categorise the frost severity of a particular site, and to compare the frost severity of different sites.

Figure 1.5 shows the mean yearly frost index for a number of sites distributed fairly uniformly across Great Britain. It can be seen that the whole of Great Britain is liable to suffer frost, ranging in severity from 8 degree days in southwest England to 177 degree days in the highlands of Scotland. Furthermore it can be remarked that every site has some frost almost every winter.

The depth of frost penetration into the ground, and into the road pavement of course where this has replaced the natural ground, measured in millimetres is given by multiplying the square root of the frost index by 50. Therefore, at a site with a frost index of 50 degree days or more, frost penetration can be expected at least 350 mm ($\sqrt{50} \times 50 = 350$) into the road pavement, which is a considerable distance into the structure. Figure 1.5 shows that this will happen over about half the country in those severe years when the mean yearly frost index represents one continuous spell of frosty weather. Roads in the whole of Great Britain are therefore potentially liable to damage from frost action in the winter, but inland, upland and northern sites are particularly at risk.

Present-day designers of roads can obtain the mean yearly frost index for any proposed site from the Meteorological Office. If the mean yearly frost index is 50 or more, all material used within the top 450 mm of the road surface must be non-frost susceptible; but if the index is less than 50, this thickness can be relaxed to 350 mm.

Frost damage to roads arises in three ways. Firstly, if there are any porous stones in the road structure, the water in the pores of the stone will freeze and the resulting 9 per cent volumetric expansion when the water changes to ice can break down the stones into smaller pieces. This process can be called *frost shattering*. Secondly, similar expansion in the voids between the stones will loosen the road structure itself – such damage occurs nowadays when the bituminous surfacing of a road is nearing the end of its useful life but must have been commonplace in the days before roads had impermeable surfacings. This process can be called *frost loosening*. The remedy for frost shattering is to exclude porous rocks from use as roadstones and this is fairly easy to ensure

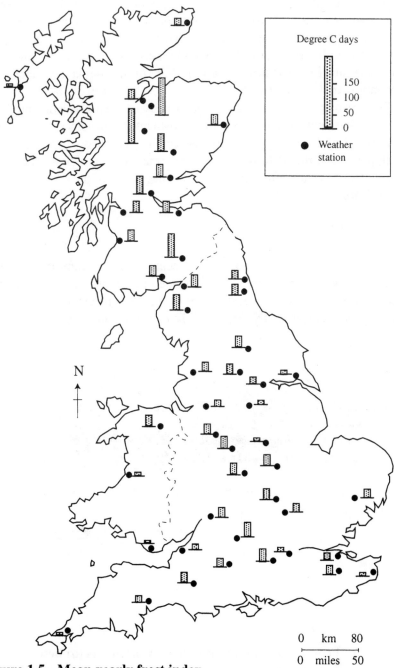

Figure 1.5   Mean yearly frost index

both now and in the past. The remedy for frost loosening is to keep water out of the road pavement by providing a waterproof surface but, as we shall see, this solution has only been possible during the twentieth century. Thirdly, and most importantly, frost damage to roads can arise from a process known as frost heave, and for present-day roads this form of frost damage is much more important than the other two kinds.

Frost heave occurs in a road structure because of the high suction produced at the freezing front when frost penetrates down into the pavement. This suction draws water up from the water table below into the zone where freezing is taking place, and this in turn leads to the formation of a thick ice lens at the freezing front as shown in Figure 1.6. The magnitude of the suction is given by the expression:

$$(s) = 4.1 + \log_{10} t$$

where s is the suction expressed on the pF scale and t is the number of degrees Celsius below freezing point. To give some idea of the size of the suction forces involved in this process, if t is only 1°C, then s is just over pF 4, which is 10^4 cm of water or 1 MN/m², which is a suction equivalent to a negative

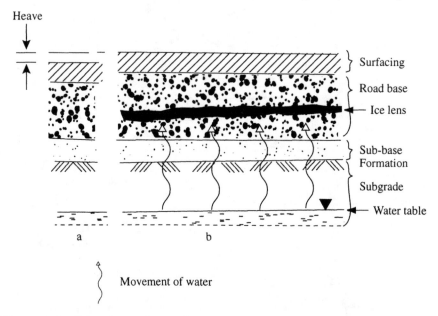

Figure 1.6   Frost heave in road pavement. Conditions (a) before freezing, and (b) during freezing

pressure of 10 atmospheres. The growth of this ice lens causes the road structure to expand upwards or heave, thus giving rise to the term frost heave. Whilst the ice lens remains frozen, the road remains capable of carrying the traffic because ice is adequately strong. But once the ice lens thaws, meltwater is released into the road structure and the road surface subsides into a pavement which is so saturated with water that it is no longer strong enough to carry the traffic loads. For frost heave to occur, as well as frost penetration there must be a water table near formation level, and the sub-base and roadbase materials must have capillaries of the right size to enable water to be drawn up. Road engineers, both now and in the past, have always tried to keep the water table well below formation level for this and other reasons. A number of times in this book we will be returning to frost damage to roads.

The understanding of frost heave and the way it damages roads was greatly advanced in the 1950s and 1960s by a series of experiments in which a full-scale road structure with a controllable water table was tested in a large refrigerated laboratory (see Figure 1.7). In particular the results confirmed, by direct measurements, that the theory of the mechanism of frost heave in roads outlined above was valid. More specifically, the results of these experiments also showed the importance of providing subgrade drains to keep the water table well below the road structure, and at a depth of at least 3 ft below the road surface, in order to minimise the likelihood of frost heave. The experiments on the road structure in the refrigerated laboratory were complemented by on-site inspections and observations of frost damage to actual roads in Great Britain in the late 1940s and during the severe winter of 1962–63.

Earthworks for Roads

Until the first part of the nineteenth century, earthworks for roads – that is cuttings and embankments – were almost nonexistent except for some causewayed roads across low-lying ground and marsh. But with the need to ease gradients for fast coach travel the first road earthworks were tentatively begun. In 1823 the Whetstone Turnpike Trustees who were responsible for the road up Barnet Hill by which the coaches from London approached the town of Barnet wanted the slope eased. James McAdam (son of the famous John Loudon McAdam), the surveyor to the Trust, raised an embankment at the foot of the slope to do this. The embankment was built of yellow clay (possibly weathered London Clay) and it slipped, McAdam admitting that

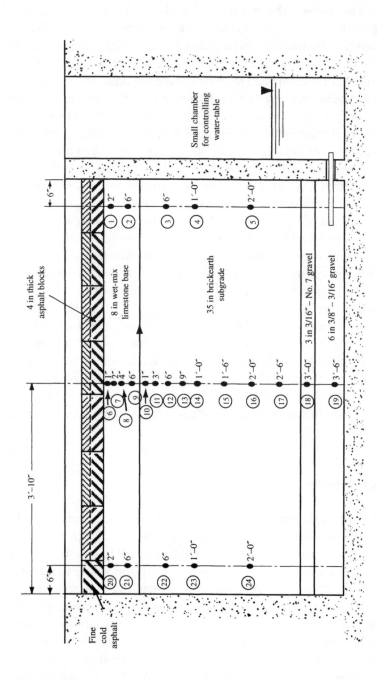

Figure 1.7   Full-scale road structure constructed beneath the floor of a large refrigerated laboratory

'he was not aware that clay would not stand at a less slope than 1 in 4'. A slope of 1 in 4 corresponds to an angle of 14°. As we shall see in chapter 8, earthworks in clay were to prove troublesome much later, on motorways.

Slips in the side slopes of both cuttings and embankments were puzzling to the early road engineers and continue to be troublesome to, and occasionally misunderstood by, present-day engineers. The crucial factor to be determined in the design of a highway side slope is its angle to the horizontal, and there are basically three ways of doing this. The first of these is trial-and-error – building slopes and finding out if they are stable or not – but the disadvantages of this method are that it is expensive, can be hazardous if the slope fails, and it takes a long time to obtain enough information to be practically useful. The second method is to examine natural hillsides in various geological formations (London Clay, Oxford Clay etc.) and determine the maximum slope angle from these. As far as the present writer knows, in spite of it being an obvious solution to the problem, this has not been done by highway engineers. The third approach is to design the slope according to the principles of soil mechanics, and this is the method used in modern times

To understand why the slope angle of an earthwork is so important, the following simplified explanation is given. Figure 1.8 shows the side slope of an highway earthwork; it can be either a cutting slope or an embankment slope. The line *AB* represents a potential slip surface, i.e. one along which the surface layer of soil of the slope can slip down the side of the cutting or embankment. In practice this potential slip surface is often curved but it is considered here to be a mainly plane surface to simplify the analysis. The zone of soil above the potential slip surface can be considered to be divided up into a number of vertical columns, one of which is shown in Figure 1.8. The forces acting on the column are its weight *W* acting vertically downward, and a shear force *S* acting parallel to the potential slip surface. The force *S* is mobilised by the tendency of the column to move down the potential slip surface, and its maximum value is determined by the shear strength of the soil. If we resolve forces along the potential slip surface, we get the condition for equilibrium of the column:

$$W \sin \theta = S$$

where θ is the angle of the slope to the horizontal. If *S* is greater than $W \sin \theta$ the slope will be stable, but if $W \sin \theta$ is greater than *S* a slip will take place. The highway engineer can do little to influence the values of *W* and *S*, the magnitudes of which are determined by physical factors, leaving the highway

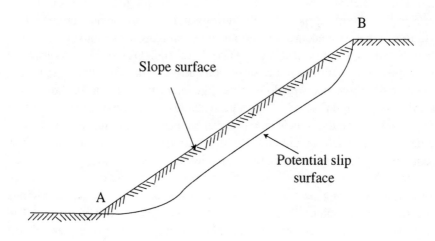

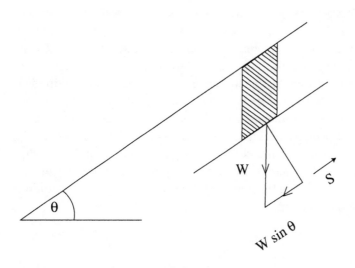

Figure 1.8   Stability of a highway earthworks slope

engineer with θ as the main parameter determining slope stability. It can be seen that, for given values of *W* and *S*, the smaller θ is, the more stable the slope will be. However, the highway engineer would like to have θ as large as possible because the greater θ is, the narrower the cutting or embankment can be and the less soil will have to be excavated, moved and compacted to form the earthworks.

There is also the question of how much land will have to be purchased to construct the road, known as the 'land take'. This is illustrated in Figure 1.9 which compares the relatively narrow land take required for a road built at ground surface (Figure 1.9a) with the much wider land take required if the road is on embankment (Figure 1.9b) or in cutting (Figure 1.9c). This consideration also means the highway engineer would like to have the side slopes as steep as possible.

In practice, the value of *S* varies during the year, being greatest when the soil is dry and the pore water pressure in the soil is low, and least when the soil is wet and the pore water pressure in the soil is high. This explains why slips on highway earthworks often occur in late winter and early spring when the soil on the slopes is in its wettest state following the winter rain. It should be noted that the large landslips that sometimes occur in nature and in very large civil engineering earthworks such as dams are often of a deep-seated rotational nature and are more complicated in their mechanism than the shallow slips discussed here.

* * *

The scope of the book has been outlined in the Preface, but a few words will be said about the timescale of the subject. The approximate range of time covered by each of the chapters, although there is necessarily some overlap, is indicated as follows:

chapter 2: 2500 BC–0: prehistoric trackways;
chapter 3: 0–500 AD: Roman roads;
chapter 4: 500–1750: medieval and later roads;
chapter 5: 1720–1770: eighteenth century roads in Scotland;
chapter 6: 1700–1900: eighteenth and nineteenth century roads;
chapter 7: 1900–1950: roads for the motor car;
chapter 8: 1950–2000: motorways.

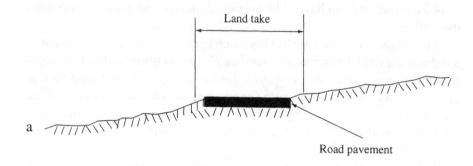

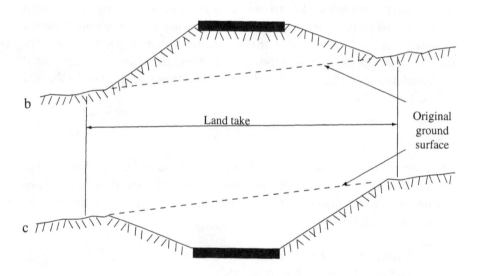

**Figure 1.9   Width of land take for road at (a) ground surface,
compared with that for road (b) on embankment, or (c) in
cutting**

As we move into the third millennium, it is becoming apparent that new roads can no longer continue to be built in Great Britain at a rate equal to the anticipated growth rate of new traffic – the 'predict and provide' policy. Therefore, in the future, the highway engineer will be mainly concerned with the maintenance, repair and renovation of existing roads rather than the construction of new ones. Consequently, present-day and future highway engineers will need to know how the existing stock of roads were built, the materials used to build them, and the different pavement structures that they possess and their characteristics. The present book serves to fill this particular practical need, as well as the other purposes mentioned in the Preface.

2   Prehistoric Trackways

O how I long to travel back,
And tread again that ancient track!

One of the most important steps in human history occurred when man changed from being a hunter-gatherer to become a farmer. The change from a nomadic life to a settled one enabled the development of all the technical arts that eventually led to civilisation. This transition marks the end of the Palaeolithic period and the beginning of the Neolithic period, about 5000 BC, and in recognition of its importance historians have called it the Neolithic Revolution. The story of roads also begins at this time.

As the new farmers established their settlements in clearings in the forests, paths would be beaten to the adjoining fields, to the nearest stream for water, to the forest for firewood, and to nearby settlements for barter and social intercourse. As these tracks became well used, the topsoil would have worn away giving place to firmer subsoil beneath and giving a better surface. It might be thought that all trace of these paths would have long since disappeared for good but, extraordinarily as it may seem, this is not the case. For in 1989 over one mile of Neolithic timber track dating from 3800 BC was uncovered in a Somerset peat bog. Named the Sweet Track after its discoverer, Raymond Sweet, the walkway was built to carry people across a swamp between two areas of dry land (Figure 2.1a). The structure of the walkway consisted of a line of logs laid end to end as a rail across which, at intervals, two long wooden pegs were driven into the peat to form a large cross; a one-foot-wide deck of planks was then attached to the upper parts of the cross (Figure 2.1b).

In course of time it would have been possible to travel a considerable distance along such a network of paths from settlement to settlement, but even so, these paths can only be considered to be the precursor of the road, the origins of which had to await a more wide-ranging, perhaps national, purpose.

By about 2500 BC the inhabitants of the British Isles were the Iberians, a people who had come originally from the Mediterranean, and who by this time had established an advanced Neolithic culture. They were pastoralists

18

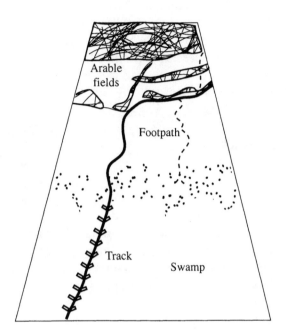

a)

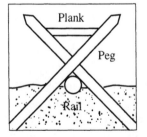

b)

Figure 2.1 **The Sweet Track in the Somerset Levels: (a) diagrammatic reconstruction; and (b) cross-section showing construction detail of the walkway**

and farmers, but also made pottery and wove cloth. They built earthwork causwayed camps, the most famous of which in Britain is Windmill Hill near Avebury in Wiltshire, in which village life is considered to have begun. The prehistoric trackways were probably first established as long-distance migration routes by the Iberians when they first arrived in Britain. The most important of the prehistoric trackways (Figure 2.2), together with estimates of their length, are described as follows.

The Principal Trackways

Icknield Way

This commences in Norfolk just inland from the Wash and proceeds in a southeasterly direction past Thetford, through Newmarket and Baldock, to Dunstable. It then follows a line close under the escarpment of the Chiltern Hills and drops down to the River Thames at Goring. Over a short section near Aston Clinton the trackway divides into an Upper and a Lower Icknield Way. The length is 132 miles.

Ridgeway

This commences at Streatley, just across the Thames from Goring, so that the Ridgeway is really a continuation of the Icknied Way. From Streatley it rises and strikes westward across the Berkshire Downs to Whitehorse Hill. Passing southeast of Swindon it turns south and crosses the Marlborough Downs and the Vale of Pewsey to reach Salisbury Plain. The length is 46 miles.

Pilgrims' Way

Commencing just north of Ashford in Kent, this runs northwest and then westward along the North Downs to just north of Redhill. From here it continues westward through Farnham, still along the North Downs, eventually leading to Salisbury Plain. The section of this trackway in Hampshire is called the Harrow Way. The length is 123 miles.

South Downs Way

From Eastbourne this route runs westward along the South Downs, through

Figure 2.2   Prehistoric trackways

Winchester to Salisbury Plain. The length is 96 miles.

Dorset Way

From the Dorset coast this route runs in a northeasterly direction past Blandford Forum and on to Salisbury Plain. The length is 46 miles.

* * *

The Iberians who landed on the southeast coast of Britain in the Dover and Eastbourne areas moved west along the Pilgrims' Way and the South Downs Way. Those who landed on the east coast in the Norfolk-Suffolk area moved a short distance inland and thence in a southwesterly direction along the Icknield way and finally westward along the Ridgeway. Those who landed on the south coast in the Dorset region moved northwest along the Dorset Way. All these routes converged on the area of the Marlborough Downs and Salisbury Plain, which in due course became a Neolithic centre of much magnitude and importance, containing – among many others – such monuments as Avebury and Stonehenge. Later, after the Iberian invasions had ceased, the trackways became highways along which the Neolithic peoples travelled to visit their monuments. Whether the stone circles of Avebury and Stonehenge be temples or observatories or even – as some wag has suggested – race courses, there can be no doubt that they were important centre of assembly for the Iberian tribes. In this sense, then, the trackways can be considered to be the first national highways in Britain, for along them moved travellers whose journeys were more than of local interest or significance.

The trackways also had a more prosaic purpose, that of trade. By about 2000 BC the mining of high-quality flint at Grime's Graves in Norfolk had commenced. These mines produced a tabular form of flint that was eagerly sought because it could be readily worked to make tools and weapons. At the surface around the mines, 'flint factories' were established where these tools and weapons were manufactured, and from the site these were exported to the rest of the country. So out from Grime's Graves along the trackways would move Neolithic travelling salesmen laden with flint tools, returning many months later with, perhaps, pottery or cloth from other regions of Britain.

The importance of the trackways to the Neolithic peoples is underlined by the presence along them of the burial chambers of their chiefs, such as Wayland's Smithy and the West Kennet Long Barrow, and also of more enigmatic monuments such as the Uffington White Horse.

In about 800 BC the Celts arrived in Britain and their invasion and westward migration mirrored that of the Iberians before them. They followed, and later used, the trackways established by the Iberians, but the extensive system of ditches that they constructed (e.g. Grim's Ditch) are not communication routes but earthworks delimiting tribal boundaries. The Celts brought with them the skills of metalliferous mining, smelting and metalworking, and the trackway that G.M. Trevelyan shows in his map of Iberian Britain as running from Salisbury Plain to the Severn Estuary (46 miles long) may be a Celtic trading route from the coast to metalliferous mines in the Carboniferous Limestone of the Mendip Hills.

The trackways were to play an important part in yet one further invasion of Britain, after which they fade from the historical scene. For in AD 43 the invading Roman army marched inland from Richborough along the Pilgrims' Way to the River Medway at Rochester where, under their commander Plautius, they defeated a British army led by Caractacus. Britain was now to become a province of the Roman Empire, and in the later campaigns of their westward invasion the Roman legions would have used the routes afforded by the trackways before they had time to construct their own roads – which are the subject of the next chapter.

In contrast to all the other roads we will be considering in this book, the trackways were not constructed roads. That is to say, they had no built surface, no pavement, no embankments or cuttings, no structures such as bridges or tunnels, and no organisation to maintain or service them. Because of this, there is little that can be discussed about them technically. Having said this, we can supply some details by intelligent speculation. As the migrating tribes moved along the trackways they would have to stop at nightfall and, no doubt, in course of time recognised camping places would become established at convenient points separated by a day's march. It has been suggested that some of the ancient earthworks, spaced at 10 mile intervals, may be these camps. Also, we would expect to see cairns or mounds set up to mark the route in open country where there were no natural features to show the way. In some places, although the one of the tracks is called the 'Ridgeway', we can note that the line of the track actually runs a little below the actual crest of the ridge – either to provide some shelter from the wind, or maybe to avoid the travellers presenting themselves as a target on the skyline for marauders. Later, when the trackways served as trade routes or routes of pilgrimage for the tribes to gather at their monuments on Salisbury Plain, local people would probably have serviced the travellers with provisions, and certain of the camps may have become centres for doing this.

It has been remarked that the prehistoric trackways are often sited on high ground, the purpose of this being to avoid the marshy lowlands and the heavily forested valleys of Britain at that time. However a glance at the geological map will show that the trackways are also commonly sited on the chalk outcrop. Partly this is a consequence of the geological structure of southern England where much of the high ground consists of the chalk because it is more resistant to weathering and erosion than the adjoining sands and clays, but partly also this is because the migrating tribes had found by trial-and-error that the chalk provided routes with the best 'going'. For the chalk downs, as the upland areas are confusingly called, being well drained and having only a thin cover of soil, provide a good all-weather surface under foot. (In this context it can be remarked that for the same reason present-day racehorse training establishments are often sited on the chalk downs, e.g. Newmarket, Lambourne.) Although the chalk downland today presents a grassland aspect, in early Neolithic times it was probably wooded, the present-day downs owing their characteristic appearance of open grassland to clearance by man (which began in the Neolithic period) followed by grazing by sheep and, before myxomatosis, rabbits. However, even the chalk woodland would have been much more penetrable than the dense forest on the sands and clays.

Later Use

The trackways did not fall entirely out of use when later roads were made. For example, the Pilgrims' Way is so called because of its much later use, in the fourteenth century, as a route to Canterbury by pilgrims travelling to the shrine of Thomas a Becket. Parts of some of the trackways remained in use as drovers' ways (often called driftways) down to the nineteenth century, and were fenced-in or hedged-in by the landowners on either side to stop the herds from wandering on to their crops or pastures. Certain lengths of the trackways have become completely incorporated into the present-day road network, as shown by parts of the Icknield Way (e.g. the main road A505 east of Baldock) and by many parts of the Pilgrims' Way in Kent. Some of the trackway routes are now designated as Long Distance Paths: these are the South Downs Way from Eastbourne to Petersfield, the North Downs Way from Dover to Farnham which follows the Pilgrims' Way, and the Ridgeway from Luton to Marlborough which follows the southern end of the Icknield Way and then the old Ridgeway.

Of all the trackways, the Ridgeway is probably the one that is closest in appearance to the old prehistoric trackways – at least in the parts where it crosses open downland away from modern civilisation. However, even here it is undergoing despoliation, for in 1987 some lengths of the Ridgeway were churned up into a quagmire by a number of so-called 'cross-country motorcyclists' whose depredations the Countryside Commission – implementers of the long-distance Ridgeway path – had not been able to stop because of a loophole in the law. The loophole arises from the fact that some ancient tracks have been designated as byways under the Wildlife and Countryside Act, 1981, an unforeseen consequence of which is that the tracks are open to all traffic. Had they been designated as bridleways, they would have been restricted to horses, cyclists and walkers. In 1994 the situation had become worse because some drivers of four-wheel-drive 'off road' vehicles had taken to using the Ridgeway as well. In 1998 a legal ruling was made that roads used as public paths could only be used by motorcycles and four-wheel-drive vehicles if it could be shown that they had been used by vehicles before 1930. The significance of the date 1930 is that the Road Traffic Act of that year, for the first time, made it an offence to drive a motorised vehicle along a public footpath or bridleway. It remains to be seen whether this ruling can protect the Ridgeway and the other trackways.

Trackways in Ireland

Some 80 small, prehistoric wooden trackways, some well over 5,000 years old, have by 1989 been located in central Ireland. Whilst several of the trackways have been known for some time, the discovery of most has been made fairly recently as a result of the stripping of peat by peat-milling machines. At Derryoghill in County Longford, 39 trackways have been found in one stretch of wetlands, the earliest dating from 2400 BC, and possibly of early or pre-Bronze Age. A further 38 prehistoric trackways have been found at Timahoe Bog in County Kildare. The most impressive trackway found to date is that crossing the Corlea Bog in County Longford, which is of the much later date of 148 BC, and therefore of Iron Age. The early tracks were up to about 8 ft wide and made of transversely split logs, placed on a foundation of irregularly placed branches laid on the bog surface. There is evidence that bronze axes had been used to cut the timber. Another form of track consisted of long straight branches placed longitudinally on the bog surface with occasional transverse supports and lateral pegs hammered into the bog surface underneath. Variations in construction included the use of tree trunks, oak planks and woven hurdles. The Corlea road is a corduroy track consisting of a solid oak plank surface and runs for over a mile across two areas of bog with a small island between them. The trackways are thought to have been communication routes between farmsteads established on the upland regions adjacent to the bogs, and are very similar in age, construction and purpose to the Sweet Track in Somerset. The Irish trackways, therefore, indicate the emergence of society in Ireland in the Neolithic period at about the same time as in England. The later Corlea road, together with its associated artifacts, shows the development of a considerable degree of economic and social organisation by the time of the Iron Age.

* * *

The invention of the wheel is, rightly, regarded as one of the greatest technological advances. The wheel seems to have emerged in Sumeria not long after 3500 BC, following which carts wagons and chariots came into use in the early Middle Eastern civilisations. These vehicles, in turn, gave rise to the need for special, hard and durable running surfaces capable of carrying concentrated loads. In this way, paths and trackways would have developed into roads. And the remaining chapters of this book deal with roads proper.

3   Roman Roads

The Roman Road runs straight and bare
As the pale parting-line in hair

For the man-in-the-street, the Romans are regarded as the exemplars of road builders, and in this instance the popular judgement is correct. For in spite of the grandeur of their other civil engineering works such as the Coliseum in Rome, their great masonry aqueducts, and their bridges, it is their roads that have become almost inseparable from the idea of the great Roman Empire itself. For the Romans had grasped the fact known to the Hittites in the fourteenth century BC and to the Chinese much later, in the third century BC, that the key to controlling an empire was a good system of roads.

As has been noted in chapter 2, the Romans invaded Britain in AD 43 and by AD 78 their conquest of England and Wales was effectively complete. During the course of this occupation they set about the construction of a network of roads which would be the means by which they would control their new province. For the Roman method of consolidating their new conquest was to plan and construct a system of military roads for the whole island, connecting together a series of forts garrisoned by regular troops. Roman roads were made for one overriding purpose – a military one. They were provided to quickly despatch troops to wherever they were needed, to give quick communication between the principal towns and the outlying garrisons and, on a wider scale, to ensure communication between the new province and Rome itself. Trade and other uses of the road were secondary to this main purpose, although as far as we know the Romans never tried to restrict their roads to official use. No doubt, however, the itinerant trader would have had to give way when a legion came swinging down the road.

Roman roads may be roughly classified into three categories: firstly, the strategic military network (Figure 3.2); secondly, a series of later roads built for general economic purposes; and thirdly, purely local roads. Probably the most well known attribute of the Roman road is its straightness, and indeed, where the geography allowed, Roman roads are remarkably straight, but where obstructions such as hills and valleys were encountered, and there was a need

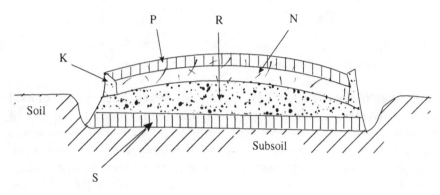

K: Kerbstones
P: Pavimentum – flat stone slabs
N: Nucleus – a layer of broken tiles and bricks
R: Rudus – a layer of compact rubble
S: Statumen – a platform of stone blocks

Figure 3.1   Cross-section of pavement structure of a Roman road – the ideal

for practicable river crossings, the Romans of course adapted the line of the roads to suit the terrain. In spite of this, what is truly remarkable is the straightness of the *overall alignment* of Roman roads, sometimes over far greater distances than could be sighted in one go; for example, the 200 mile Roman road from Axminster to Lincoln that we now call the Fosse Way never deviates by more than eight miles from the direct line. However, in upland and mountain areas Roman roads followed winding valley bottoms or ridge tops, but even in these circumstances they were built as a series of short straight sections; terraces and zigzags were used to negotiate steep slopes. It has been estimated that the Roman road system in Britain probably totalled about 10,000 miles at the end of their period of occupation of the island, of which most were probably built in the first 100 years.

The Roman roads were built by the Roman army, but there was no specialised corps of engineers like the Royal Engineers of the British Army: rather, each legion of the Roman army included road building as integral part of its military duties and many of the roads were constructed on active service during campaigns. Here lies a clue, perhaps, to why the Roman roads were made so straight. It may have been for the benefit of a number of small, independent detachments of relatively unskilled soldiers who would have had little difficulty in sighting themselves onto a line between distant beacons set up beforehand by more experienced surveyors.

Structure of the Roman Road

The idealised, elaborate pavement structure of a Roman road often used to illustrate books on Roman history (Figure 3.1) was not used for roads outside cities and towns other than for prestige projects, and then only when the appropriate materials were available. In Britain, far simpler road construction was practised using locally available materials.

The first step in road construction was to clear trees, brush and other vegetation from a wide swathe extending on either side of the proposed line. The purpose of this was tactical, namely to provide a safeguard for troops on the road from ambush or surprise attack. A basal layer of large stones, often the ubiquitous flints in southeast Britain, was then laid; these stones were probably field stones gathered from the cleared swathe. The purpose of this layer of stones is not known – the Romans may have thought of it as a foundation – but with hindsight we can see that it formed a horizontal drainage layer for the road structure above. Two continuous, deep ditches were then dug on either side of the road and the spoil from the ditches was thrown into the centre and compacted over the basal layer to form a low embankment or causeway called the *agger* (Figure 3.3). The purpose of this was also tactical; it was to give troops on the road an advantageous defensive position if attacked, but it had the immense technical benefit of draining the road and keeping the surface and pavement structure relatively dry. It may be, then, that the Romans hit upon the first principle of roadmaking – good drainage – as the accidental by-product of a military requirement. The road pavement was laid on top of the agger, and usually consisted of a base layer of stones covered with a surface layer of gravel, but the materials used depended entirely on what was available locally. In the Wealden district of southeast England, slag from the local iron smelting was used.

The Roman road between Salisbury and Dorchester has been the subject of archaeological excavation at a number of places. On one section, the agger was made by compacting chalk over a basal layer of large flints, and the pavement was constructed of gravel obtained from one and a half miles away; but on another section, although the structure was identical, the surface of the road itself was of was made of chalk. A third section of road revealed an

Figure 3.2   **Main Roman roads in Britain**

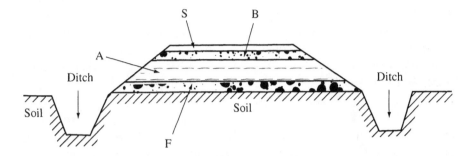

S: Surface layer of gravel
B: Base layer of stones
A: Agger – spoil excavated from the ditches
F: Foundation of large stones

Figure 3.3   Cross-section of pavement structure of a Roman road – in practice

agger made from a mixture of chalk, gravel and soil put together in a rough and ready manner. Although there must have been overall direction of the building of the whole road, the actual detail of construction seems to have been left to the squad of soldiers on the section, and depended on what materials were locally available. These examples have been from the soft rock area of Britain.

By contrast, in the hard rock area of Britain, the Roman road crossing Wheeldale Moor in North Yorkshire is paved with stone slabs obtained from a local flagstone outcrop – thus showing that the soldiers could and did build *pavimentum*, even out on the moors, where the right materials were to hand – and providing us with a surviving example. In many places in the hard rock area of Britain the intractability of the rocks precluded both the construction of aggers and the digging of ditches. In Cumbria, excavation of Roman roads has revealed that construction details varied enormously: their widths change, they are embanked in places and not in others, they may or may not be metalled, and if they were, local materials were always used and varied from beach pebbles to quarried rock. Furthermore, the alignments are better described as direct rather than straight. The impression gained is that great latitude was allowed to the engineers, depending on local circumstances.

The road now known locally as Wade's Causeway, situated south of Goathland in North Yorkshire, has been described as the longest and best preserved section of Roman road in Great Britain and it is about one and a quarter miles long. The road is 16 feet wide and raised in the centre, with ditches on either side. In places the top surface has eroded away leaving an abundance of large stone blocks visible, but it is hard to say whether these are stones from the basal layer or whether they are all that remains of the agger.

Two further cross sections through the pavements of Roman roads are shown in Figure 3.4, with dimensions given for the various layers in mm as measured in the modern archaeological excavations. The first, Figure 3.4a, is of the Fosse Way near Radstock in Somerset, and shows that for this important road the Romans had used concrete for the *rudus* and the *nucleus*. The cement used to make the concrete was probably lime-based and it is likely that it was manufactured locally. The total thickness of pavement was a massive 863 mm (almost 3 ft). The Fosse Way was a Roman main road and the pavement structure shows that it was constructed to their highest standard (compare Figures 3.1 and 3.4a). The second cross-section, Figure 3.4b, is from a road through the Medway Valley near Rochester in Kent. This road was on poor

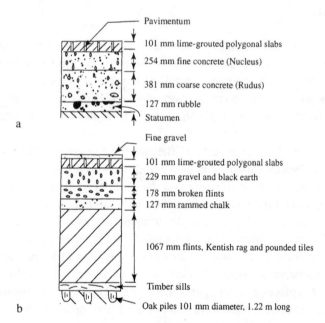

a

Pavimentum
101 mm lime-grouted polygonal slabs
254 mm fine concrete (Nucleus)
381 mm coarse concrete (Rudus)
127 mm rubble
Statumen

b

Fine gravel
101 mm lime-grouted polygonal slabs
229 mm gravel and black earth
178 mm broken flints
127 mm rammed chalk

1067 mm flints, Kentish rag and pounded tiles

Timber sills
Oak piles 101 mm diameter, 1.22 m long

Figure 3.4   Cross-sections of pavement structures of Roman roads at (a) Radstock, and (b) the Medway Valley

ground where swampy soils were encountered. In this case oak piles had been driven into the soft soil and covered with timber sills before some 1.7 m (about 5.5 ft) thickness of pavement was constructed. Much of this great thickness of pavement was probably to raise the level of the road surface well above the swamp, and the purpose of the piles and sills was to support the large thickness of roadmaking material which would have otherwise sunk into the swamp.

Before leaving the subject of the construction of Roman roads one further observation will be conjectured. It was remarked above that we do not know what was the purpose of the basal layer of stones beneath the agger, and it may well be that it was not a part of the Roman construction at all. It is possible that the Romans occasionally built their road on top of a previous pre-Roman road, of which the basal layer of stones is all that remains. If this is the case, then it both explains the presence of the basal layer and indicates that the British tribes may have practised the art of roadmaking before the Romans came to Britain.

* * *

Roman roads varied considerably in their dimensions. Where provided, the agger was always much wider than the surfaced pavement. On the main roads in southern Britain the roads were 80 ft wide between the drainage ditches and the pavement was 20-30 ft wide with aggers twice as wide. The height of the agger also varied, being typically 2-3 ft but sometimes as much as 6-8 ft.

During the long time that the Romans were in Britain the roads would have required maintenance and repair. Sections that have been excavated across Roman roads often reveal areas that have been patched and overlaid, sometimes several times, and replacement lengths of road laid alongside the original alignment.

It has been said of Roman roads that they were over-engineered – that 'they were built with a tremendous waste of materials and labour'. This is not wholly fair. The earthworks of the agger and ditches were primarily for tactical defence purposes, although as we have seen, they also served the admirable purpose of drainage. It is true that the pavement had only to support marching men and light horse rigs but the depth and solidity of construction ensured a long life. Also, the Roman roads were in use for a very long time and the pavement structure we see today in archaeological excavations may represent accretions of material from periodic road maintenance which we know the Romans carried out (see above). The straight alignments were mainly found in lowland Britain, but in highland Britain the alignments often followed the routes that were easiest to build. Where wheel ruts have been preserved in the surface of Roman roads, they are usually found in the middle, indicating that traffic was generally light enough for vehicles to be able to keep to the crown of the road.

As well as obtaining their construction materials locally, the Romans also opened quarries for building stone and roadstone. One such quarry was at Blunsdon Ridge near Swindon in Wiltshire. Here, from the earliest days of the occupation, the Romans quarried limestone for use in the surrounding region. One interesting fact preserved at this quarry is that on the road leading into and out of the workings, the fully-laden wagons leaving the quarry made deeper ruts than the empty wagons returning, and thereby indicating that the wagons kept to the left – perhaps showing that our rule of the road goes back a long time.

The Main Roman Roads

In southern Britain there were six main roads, all radiating from London (Figure 3.2). Using their anglicised names, and going clockwise, these were:

> Ermine Street running north to Lincoln, York and on to Scotland;
> four shorter roads terminating at Caister St Edmund (near Norwich), Dover, Chichester and Dorchester respectively;
> Watling Street which ran northwest to Wroxeter, from which there was a connection to Chester.

In addition there were two main cross-country roads, the Fosse Way which ran from Ilchester via Bath, Cirencester and Leicester to Lincoln, and the shorter Akeman Street which ran from St Albans to Cirencester linking the Fosse Way to Watling Street and, thereby, to London.

Comparing Figure 3.2 with succeeding maps in this book shows that the radial plan of roads centred on London which was to be so apparent later, and which still persists to the present day, was established by the Roman road network.

In northern Britain there were three main roads north of Hadrian's wall – the main one from Corbridge to Inveresk being known as Dere Street. North of the Antonine Wall there was one short main road from Camelon to just beyond Perth.

4   The Years of Neglect

The rolling English drunkard
made the rolling English road

The end of Roman rule in Britain did not occur on a specific date like, say, the end of British rule in an African colony after the Second World War. Rather, there was a long period during which rule from Rome gradually declined, leaving effective power in the hands of provincial governors, some of whom became self-styled 'emperors'. The final, declining episode of Roman rule commenced in AD 410 when the Emperor Honorius was unable to respond to a request from Britain for military reinforcements, leaving the garrison in the province on its own resources, and concluded in AD 426 when the Emperor Valentinian III withdrew all the remaining Roman regular troops. Thus ended almost four centuries of Roman rule in Britain.

With the downfall of Roman power, the island became prey to raids of increasing boldness by seafaring bands of Angles, Saxons and Jutes from their homelands across the North Sea. Once the Roman legions had departed, the Roman roads which had been the primary means of holding the province now served as the prime agents of its downfall. The longships of the sea-raiders that had brought them across the North Sea could be taken well upstream on the main rivers; from here bands of warriors could disembark and move swiftly across country utilising the excellent Roman road system, bent on their mission of plunder and destruction. We can imagine that the Saxon raiding parties could not have believed their luck when they first found the stone causeways leading them in to the interior.

From about AD 450 onwards, the invasions took on a different nature as the Angles, Saxons and Jutes poured across the North Sea not to raid but to settle, and by the end of the sixth century we have a recognisable Anglo-Saxon nation. Later came the Danes, who also started by raiding and then, like their Anglo-Saxon predecessors, began to settle. After much warring between the two, a united kingdom – England – was established by Canute in the years 1017–35. King Canute deserves mention in this book for another reason – as a road builder – for he had constructed a causewayed road between Peterborough and Ramsey, known as the 'King's Delf'.

It is probably at about this period that the most important of the old Roman roads received their rather quaint English names that we still use today:

London via Lincoln to York: Ermine Street;
St Albans to Cirencester: Akeman Street;
Ilchester to Lincoln: Fosse Way;
London to Wroxeter: Watling Street.

It is likely that a network of byways developed at this time, because the Anglo-Saxons and the Danes settled in small villages rather than towns, and this pattern of settlement calls for a system of small roads running from hamlet to village, and village to market, rather than one major roads running from city to city as the Roman system had done. The new roads were probably all unpaved and, particularly on clay soils, would have been almost impassable to vehicles in the winter; some were no more than footpaths or bridlepaths. They were not laid out as the Roman roads were, but wandered around the countryside avoiding even minor obstructions – and therefore have a characteristic wandering nature.

In 1066 the newly elected English King Harold faced two almost simultaneous invasions from two competing claimants to his throne – Harald Hardrada, King of Norway, and William, Duke of Normandy. Although Harold was expecting the first blow to fall from the Normans on the south coast, it was Hardrada who landed first, in the north near York. Harold with his mounted infantry rode north and defeated Hardrada at Stamford Bridge. Three days later William landed at Pevensey and Harold and his force rode back in four days to rally his southeast army for the stand against the Normans at Hastings which ended in his defeat. The distance from York to London is 170 miles as the crow flies, so to cover it in four days would have necessitated riding more than 40 miles each day; and it was in October. It seems certain that if it were not for the Roman roads (principally Ermine Street), Harold and his force would not have been able to move so swiftly to deal with these threats coming at the same time at opposite ends of his kingdom. The legacy of the Roman Empire in Britain was to serve the later English Kingdom in its hour of peril – but in vain.

Following the Conquest came the imposition of Norman rule and customs on England. At first thought it might be supposed that William would have had need for a system of military roads, like the Romans before, in order to control his new kingdom, but as far as we know, although the Normans built many castles to dominate the country, they built no new roads. Perhaps the

Roman roads were still in good enough condition to serve their needs adequately. Also it can be remarked, the Normans relied on cavalry for their main military force, rather than infantry as the Romans had done, and cavalry can move swiftly across country with less dependence on roads than infantry which needs good roads to move quickly. So the Normans probably had less need of a good road system than had the Romans.

The Normans brought with them to England the practice of building in stone, whereas before them the Anglo-Saxons and Danes had, apart from their churches, built mainly in timber. The new vogue for building in stone had a disastrous effect on Roman buildings and roads because, in many instances, they became 'quarries' for building stone. This is the reason why today many Roman roads exist only as an agger or a line, and all trace of the pavement has disappeared.

Medieval Roads

Once it had been successfully imposed, one of the ways in which Norman rule was consolidated in England was by the establishment of monastic houses in different parts of the country. These establishments often had numerous scattered estates and the monks were granted free passage between them for the transport of goods. It is well known that the construction and maintenance of bridges were carried out by the monastic orders, and indeed were regarded as particularly pious acts in themselves. But it is not known whether the monasteries were road builders as well. There is no historical evidence that any of the abbeys were ever involved in the construction of roads on a large scale, but it is reasonable to suppose that they would not have built bridges without concerning themselves with the attendant roads, because the bridges by themselves would have been of little use. There seems little doubt that the skills required to build the abbeys' medieval stone bridges would have more than sufficed to make simple metalled roads. One piece of indirect evidence for the existence of medieval roads is that monastic and other legal documents sometimes mention roads as defining the boundaries of property. In and around medieval towns and cities, the dominant type of road construction that developed consisted of cobbles or roughly dressed small blocks of stone bedded on a foundation of sand, and sometimes bound together with mortar. Figure 4.1 shows such road construction in progress outside the walls of a medieval city and indicates some of the techniques in use at the time. The city shown is probably in continental Europe, maybe the Low Countries, and not in Britain,

Figure 4.1 Medieval road construction
(The author and publisher apologise for the poor quality of this figure.)

but it gives an impression of what could be done. Away from the towns and cities, the roads were of earth or, at best, gravel.

Turning to non-ecclesiastical roads, the medieval period saw the beginnings of settled life and the development of trade between towns and villages, necessitating means of communication and transport. To begin with, a road in medieval times was not an engineered construction, nor even a narrow strip of land with defined boundaries. Rather it was a generalised right to pass from one place to the next – a sort of 'right-of-way' – which over the passage of time would become a single track where the going was good. However, where the going was not good, the traveller would divert to one side or the other, leading to the development of wide swathe of land with multiple tracks.

It has been said that medieval roads made themselves, but it is truer to say that they were made by their traffic. In summer when the ground was reasonably dry, the hooves of horses and the wheels of carts would have compacted the soil and roughly levelled the surface to give a passably smooth earth road. But in winter when the ground was wet, the same traffic would have cut the surface up and churned the soil to mud. It is probably true to say that most earth roads in lowland Britain would have been impassable in wet winters.

Travellers on medieval roads went on foot or, if they were wealthy, on horseback. The great majority of freight, whether raw materials or goods, was carried by packhorse, as is recalled today by inns called 'The Packhorse' or 'The Packsaddle' in various parts of the country, and by road names such as 'The Packway'. Carts were used infrequently and even then they were mainly for taking material about locally rather than for long distance transport.

There was one other authority in the land that could have taken a lead in constructing medieval roads and that was the king. In medieval times, during the summer months, the king was usually on the move from place to place throughout his kingdom. There were at least three reasons for this. Firstly, to assert his authority over his dukes, earls and barons and scotch any plots against him. Secondly, to hold legal courts for the settlement of grievances and the administration of justice. Thirdly, to show himself to his people and thereby consolidate his rule. The king, of course, travelled with his courtiers, and an extensive retinue was needed so that they could travel in style. The king, therefore, would have been very acutely aware of the shortcomings of the highways, and would himself have been one of the principal sufferers from the parlous state of the roads. In spite of this, there is no record of any of the kings ordering or commissioning major road construction during medieval times – and this constitutes an historical question for which there is no answer.

Another type of road came into being in the later Middle Ages period and this is the drove road, made to facilitate the long distance movement of cattle and sheep. Drove roads were for delivering livestock to market and were located primarily where good grazing and overnight pasture was available. The often kept to high ground above the farmland in the valleys. Drove roads were often very wide in order to accommodate the flocks and also sometimes very straight in alignment. Ones that have been incorporated into the modern road system are recalled today by road names such as 'The Driftway'.

The dissolution of the monasteries in 1536–39 by Henry VIII effectively brings to an end the medieval period. The breaking up and dispersal of the monastic orders also removed the only organisation in medieval times that had ever concerned itself with road building and there was nothing to replace it. From this time until the coming of the turnpike trusts in the early eighteenth century virtually nothing was done about the nation's roads.

Statute Labour

Responsibility for the maintenance of such roads that did exist in medieval and later times fell upon the parishes, each one of which had to look after the roads within its boundaries. Each parish elected a surveyor of highways, who served unpaid for one year, and who had to get from each able-bodied man in the parish four days of labour on appointed days. He could also require farmers or landowners to provide carts, horses and materials at the same time. Neither the surveyor nor his workforce usually had any roadmaking ability or skills. This system rarely worked properly – the surveyor was resented by those he had to call upon to do the work so that the job was unpopular – and those so pressed as labourers resented giving their labour for nothing. Often the four days provided an opportunity for skylarking during which perhaps a little work was done. As early as 1555 an attempt was made to legally codify the parish system of road maintenance by a Statute of Highways passed by Philip and Mary (2 & 3 Philip and Mary, c.8) which set out the duties of the surveyor of highways, the level of labour and materials to be provided, the fines or penalties to be imposed on defaulters, and the duties of the justices of the peace in enforcing compliance. This system of road maintenance and repair was known as *statute labour* and persisted well into the nineteenth century. It is interesting to note that a similar system, known as *la corvee*, existed in France before the Revolution, and was just as unsatisfactory as its British equivalent. With hindsight, it can be seen that there were three factors that ensured the failure of statute labour, and *la corvee*. These were firstly, that it was forced on the reluctant parishioners at their own expense; secondly, that where a major highway passed through the parish the local community resented having to maintain a road for the benefit mainly of people passing through; and thirdly, that the neither surveyor nor workforce were professional road builders.

The following details of statute labour on the roads are for the county of Perthshire in Scotland in 1760. Those persons liable for statute labour on the roads were summoned at church service on Sunday and were required to work for three days before and three days after harvest. The working day was eight hours. Each working party consisted of 20 men, each of whom was expected to bring the required tools. Also, a cart had to be provided together with driver and loader. Those liable for statute labour could commute their obligation for service by making a money payment instead. The commutation ranged from 6d per day up to 2s per day depending on the extent of the individual's obligation.

The Commonwealth

During the latter part of the Commonwealth period (1649–60) it is not surprising to find that Oliver Cromwell turned his attention to the condition of the roads, because for a centralised, military authority such as his state was, a good road system was imperative to consolidate and safeguard his rule. Accordingly he took two steps: he appointed a Surveyor-General of Highways together with appropriate funding; and he prepared a parliamentary bill for repairing the highways and improving the public roads. These measures would have replaced statute labour with a central authority responsible for roads throughout Great Britain. Unfortunately for the roads, in 1657 Cromwell dismissed parliament before these measures could be put into effect, and in the high drama of the succeeding events – Cromwell's death and the Restoration – all consideration of the state of the roads was swept into the background.

Daniel Defoe's Tour

As the seventeenth century drew to a close, and with it an increase in personal travel, the condition of roads started to attract attention. One of the first travellers to complain about the parlous state of England's roads was Celia Fiennes, who rode on horseback through every county in England between 1685 and 1703, making a somewhat idiosyncratic survey of the whole country. From her journal of this time we get accounts of the poor road conditions in the 1690s. Here is an extract from her diary describing a journey on the main road from Reading to Newbury in Berkshire: 'From Reading to Theale 5 mile sad clay deep way, thence to Newbury 8 mile all clay mirey ground'.

In the early years of the eighteenth century the writer Daniel Defoe made a tour of Great Britain which he made a survey of geographical, social and economic conditions throughout the country, and recorded how people lived and earned their living. He wrote an account of his tour in a book which was published in three volumes between 1724 and 1726 and which has become a classic source for historians. Like Celia Fiennes before him, Defoe travelled on horseback, and amongst the many observations Defoe made he recorded the condition of the nation's roads, of which he was especially critical. Heavy goods were not moved by road but there was traffic in packages using a service of eight-horse stage wagons that trundled laboriously from inn to inn churning up the mud and leaving deep ruts. There was also a government-run mail service which utilised riders carrying mail pouches from post house to post house, changing horses *en route*. Perceptively, Defoe noted that the worst highways were those that went across clay soils, and he observed that the real problem with most of Britain's highways was that they were not properly made-up roads but simply ways across country. He pointed out to his countrymen that the last people in the land to build roads with stone had been the Romans. In Defoe's time the parishes were responsible for the maintenance of any highways that passed through them, but Defoe found that this often amounted to no more than dumping rubbish into the deepest holes. Defoe considered that the new turnpike trusts offered the best prospect for improving the highways, although when he made his tour there were only about thirty of them in existence. Defoe died in 1731 so he did not live to see the great flowering of stone road construction that came to pass later in the eighteenth century and which is described in chapter 6.

* * *

However, not all the turnpike trusts made a good job of their roads, some being content to collect the tolls without doing much road construction or road maintenance. In 1770 Arthur Young published his *Six Months' Tour* in which he gave a description of some of the roads in the north of England.

Speaking of two of the turnpike roads that he travelled along, he warned other travellers that 'They will here meet with ruts, which I actually measured four feet deep, and floating with mud. The only mending it (the road) receives is tumbling some loose stones, which serve no other purpose than jolting a carriage'. He went on to say that he had passed three broken down carts within a distance of 18 execrable miles. On the second road, at one place he had to hire two men to support his chaise in order to prevent it from overturning. We shall be meeting Arthur Young again in chapter 6.

The statue labour roads were just as bad, if not worse. As late as 1809 dreadful roads could still be found in England and we will end this chapter with a description of a badly made and ill-maintained road from that year. The top drawing in Figure 4.2 shows the most common form of a road when newly made up; it was constructed simply by throwing the soil from the ditches into the centre of the roadway and shaping it into a convex profile with a high camber. The idea of the high camber was to shed rainwater. However, because of this the carriages and waggons were forced to run entirely on the crown of the road to avoid toppling sideways. As a consequence the centre of the road became ploughed into deep ruts which retained rainwater in spite of the high camber, and the condition of the road eventually took on the form of the second drawing in Figure 4.2. The parish highway surveyor would then contract a stout labourer to repair the road which he did by filling in the ruts with whatever material was to hand, restoring the high camber ('barrelling' it was called) and raking a little gravel over the finished surface. The road was then in the condition shown in the third drawing in Figure 4.2. Once again vehicles were constrained to run on the crown of the road and the process of deterioration once more ran its course. The bottom drawing in Figure 4.2 shows the final condition of the road, reached by the second or third year after the repair.

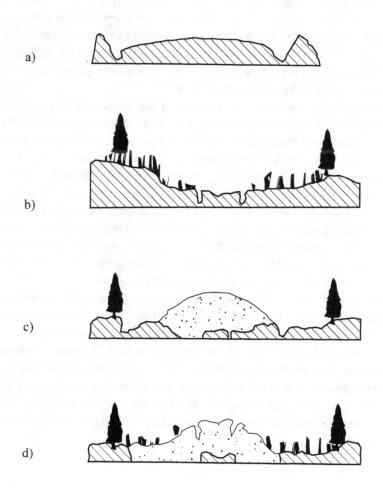

Figure 4.2   **Statute labour road, 1809**
a)   **Profile of road as newly formed**
b)   **After a year's service**
c)   **Immediately after repair**
d)   **Two or three years after repair**

5   Scotland's Military Roads

If you had seen these roads before they were made,
You would hold up your hands and bless General Wade.

In 1603, when James VI of Scotland became James I of England, the kingdoms
of Scotland and England were united in the monarchy but still otherwise
retained separate identities, including having separate parliaments. The
question of a more complete union between the two countries than that of the
union of the crowns was answered by Oliver Cromwell during the
Commonwealth (1649–59) who simply annexed Scotland to England by
military force. This union was short lived and was dissolved after the
Restoration. The question of a union, however, emerged again and after much
heated debate and discussion the Act of Union was passed by the parliaments
of both Scotland and England in 1707 and the two nations became one –
taking the anglicised name of the old Roman province, Britannia, but adding
an adjective to it – Great Britain. The new nation had a single parliament, and
a new national flag was even produced, devised by superimposing the cross
of St George on the cross of St Andrew to symbolise the new union.

The union of Scotland and England, however, did not mean that all in
Scotland were content. Those that did not like the new arrangements found
ready allies in the Jacobites – those who still looked to the exile pretender,
James VIII, as their true king. A major uprising took place took place in
September 1715 but was defeated in November; although James landed in
Scotland in December, his cause was lost and, the rebellion over, he was
forced to return to France in February 1716.

Wade

The rising of 1715 greatly troubled the new British parliament and in 1725 a
Disarming Act was passed which forbade the highlanders, many of whom
had supported the rebellion, to carry arms and required them to hand in any
they already possessed. However, because of the remoteness and inaccessibility

of the Scottish highlands the Act had little effect. In July 1724 Major-General George Wade was sent to Scotland to investigate how the law for disarming the highlanders could be better enforced. His report concluded that the greatest obstacle was 'the want of roads and bridges'. The not unexpected result was that in December 1724 Wade was appointed Commander-in-Chief for North Britain, provided with troops and finance, and told to construct forts, garrisons and barracks, together with the roads and bridges necessary to maintain communication between them, throughout the highlands. Accordingly, Wade set about building a series of forts linked by military roads. When Wade left Scotland in 1740 he had supervised the construction of 235 miles of road and 28 bridges. Wade was promoted to field-marshal in 1743, died at the age of 75 and was buried in Westminster Abbey.

Caulfeild

Wade's work was carried on by his successor, Major William Caulfeild. Caulfeild was a subaltern in charge of one of Wade's working parties in 1732 when he came to the notice of the general. He was promoted to major and made Inspector of Roads in the same year, holding this post until his death in 1767. Caulfeild carried on with Wade's work, completing the construction of the forts and some further 800–900 miles of road. Caulfeild was succeeded by Colonel Skene, and by 1784 some 1100 miles of military road and 815 bridges had been built. The complete network of roads is shown in Figure 5.1. All of these roads were built primarily for military use, and all save one were in the highlands: the exception is the road in Dumfries and Galloway which had nothing to do with subduing the highlanders but was built to facilitate the movement of troops to and from Ireland.

How the Military Roads were Made

The military roads in the highlands were constructed by soldiers, but except for the engineer officers, these were not specialists like our present-day sappers – rather, they were ordinary soldiers from infantry regiments. The first task was to make a survey of the line of the road. A typical survey party consisted of an engineer officer, a noncommissioned officer and six other ranks: they were equipped with one theodolite and a chain. When the line had been fixed construction could commence. Camps were set up at 10 mile intervals from

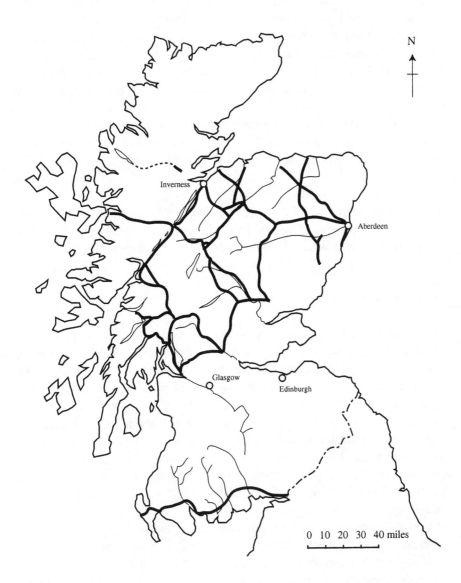

Figure 5.1   Scotland's military roads

which the work was done. A typical working party consisted of one captain, two subalterns, two sergeants, two corporals, one drummer and 100 men. When engaged on road construction every soldier received extra pay – for the noncommissioned ranks road work meant double pay! In addition to the military personnel, there were some civilian workers for tasks involving special skills, mainly masons, wallers, pavers, carpenters, and blacksmiths. The tools used included shovels, pickaxes, spades, crowbars, screwjacks, wheelbarrows, sledgehammers, small cranes and gunpowder. Material for constructing the roads abounded everywhere in the highlands. Stones in a variety of sizes were easily obtained, and large boulders could be removed from the road line and reduced to usable pieces by breaking them up with sledgehammers or by the use of gunpowder. In most locations, gravel for the finished road surface was also readily available from nearby deposits of glacial, or alluvial gravel.

Road construction was confined to the period April to October and a 10-hour day was often worked. Some 1.5–2 yards per man per day seems to have been the rate of progress. Usually the roads were built in a straight line except where steep ascents were encountered and here zigzags were used.

Structure of the Military Road

The width of the military roads was 16 ft. This was extraordinarily wide for the time and is wider than marching men would need. The roads were not intended for coach traffic and it seems that the most likely explanation for the width is that it was required for the passage of artillery. The structure of a typical military road is shown in Figure 5.2. The first step in the construction of a such a road was to excavate a shallow trench about 2 ft deep along the line of the road and across its full width. The spoil from this trench was thrown to either side and formed into two banks flanking the road. In the bottom of the trench a layer of large stones was laid to form the foundation of the pavement. On top of this foundation a middle layer of smaller stones was laid and compacted. Then a surface layer of gravel, also well compacted, was laid to form the running surface. Finally, two side drains were dug on the outsides of the banks; from their position we can infer that the purpose of these drains was not to drain water away from the road itself but, rather, to intercept runoff from the surrounding ground and prevent it from flowing across the road. When the road was on sloping ground, it was necessary to allow the water from the upslope drain to pass across to the downslope drain and open cross-drains were provided from place to place (one is shown in Fig 5.2). In the wet

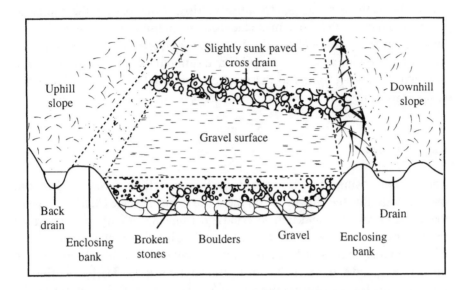

Uphill slope

Downhill slope

Slightly sunk paved cross drain

Gravel surface

Back drain

Drain

Enclosing bank

Broken stones

Boulders

Gravel

Enclosing bank

Figure 5.2   Pavement structure of a Scottish military road

climate of the highlands, water was an ever present enemy of the road and every year re-gravelling of the surface, repair of the cross drains and cleaning of the side drains had to be carried out. In locations where hard bedrock was just below the surface, it is likely that digging the trench was dispensed with and the road pavement was laid after just removing the topsoil.

* * *

The construction of the military roads started in 1725, the year following Wade's appointment, and this considerably predates the work of the famous eighteenth-century roadmakers to be described in the next chapter. Also, comparison of Figures 3.3 and 5.2 shows that Wade's road structure differed from that of the Romans. Therefore Wade's methods must have been devised by himself and his engineer-officers.

The military roads would, of course, have been subjected to severe frosts in the winter. The maximum frost index for the Scottish highlands is 177 degree days, thus giving a frost penetration of $\sqrt{77} \times 50$ mm which is 665 mm or 26 in. The thickness of the pavement was about 2 ft, which is just about enough to prevent the zero isotherm penetrating into the soil beneath the road except in the worst winters. Wade's pavement therefore effectively protected the soil beneath the road from frost heave. Most of the rocks in the highlands that would have been used to make the roads are non-porous so that the stones making up the pavement would have been unlikely to suffer from frost shattering. However, the roads would have suffered from frost loosening and this may have contributed to the maintenance problems that we know the roads experienced.

Later History

The Jacobite rising of 1745 – the Forty-Five Rebellion – was the last, but most serious, that the British government had to face. Prince Charles Stewart, the son of James VIII, landed in Scotland and, using the military roads provided by the British government, proceeded to collect his clansmen supporters and took complete control of Scotland. Against the advice of his chiefs he then invaded England and marched with an army as far south as Derby, but finding little support for his cause, retreated to Scotland. A British army under the Duke of Cumberland was despatched after him and in 1746 the terrible battle of Culloden sealed Charles' fate and he left for exile again in France. His father died in 1766 and he took the title of Charles III. After the fright engendered by the Forty-Five, the British government returned to military construction in the highlands with renewed zeal, the prime example of which is the splendid Fort George, near Inverness, which took 24 years to build and was completed in 1769; it was for a long time the largest construction ever undertaken in the highlands. The military roads and smaller forts were also refurbished and extended. However, happily, these military works were never required to be used in anger for the government did not have to deal with another rising. As the rest of the eighteenth century unfolded, peace settled over the highlands and although the military roads were still maintained by the Army, they became gradually used more for civilian traffic. This often necessitated re-grading, or realigning, portions of the roads which were too steep or had too tight bends for the carriages that became an important element in civil transport towards the end of the eighteenth century.

As the 1,100 miles of road gradually changed from military to civilian use, the government sought to divest itself of the responsibility and cost of maintaining them. The obvious step was to make the counties responsible for maintaining the roads. A Highland Road and Bridge Act of 1810 empowered the counties to raise revenue from landowners to do this. However, this was unpopular for through roads that were of national rather than local importance, which therefore became a national charge under a 1814 Act. With the advent of turnpike roads and their traffic of fast stage coaches, the military roads became subsumed into the general road network. Today, the alignments of many of them are still in use as the basis of our modern roads. Those military roads that have been abandoned and whose stone surfaces have been reclaimed by nature can sometimes still be recognised today by their remaining twin banks of earth running in parallel straight lines across the country.

* * *

The military roads in Scotland are the only example since Roman times of a network of roads being built for military purposes in Great Britain. Even during the great crises of the Civil War, the Napoleonic War, the Great War and the Second World War the ordinary network of civil roads proved sufficient for military traffic, no additional major road construction having taken place during these periods.

Finally, there is an irony of history in the fact that the Scottish military roads, which were intended to serve the British government in its policy of subduing the Jacobites, turned out to be of so much use to Prince Charles in his attempt to re-establish the Stewart monarchy.

6 Eighteenth and Nineteenth Century Roads

And where his Roads
In beautiful and sinuous line far seen

The eighteenth century saw the commencement of the great age of empirical road construction in Great Britain associated with the names of Metcalf, McAdam and Telford. But to trace the origins of this development we must, surprisingly, start in France with the great French road engineer Tresaguet. The flowering of road construction in the mid-eighteenth century had several causes. Firstly, advances in manufacture and commerce led to growing prosperity – at least among the upper classes – and this together with peace and political stability at home made travel a more needful and desirable activity, both for business and for pleasure. Secondly, the development of the horse-drawn coach – first at Kocs in northwest Hungary from where we derive the word 'coach' – but later in other parts of Europe, including Great Britain, with their light construction and narrow-rimmed wheels called for a much smoother running surface than roads had possessed hitherto. Thirdly, there was the need of the government for swift postal communication between Great Britain and Ireland for administrative purposes. Fourthly, and not least, some exceptionally able men, seeing the necessity of good roads, applied their minds to the art and science of roadmaking.

Tresaguet

Pierre-Marie-Jerome Tresaguet was born in 1716 in the town of Nevers, into a family of Bourbonnais and Nivernais origin. His father, who held the appointment of a royal engineer in the town of Moulins, had three children, also engineers or architects. In many ways Tresaguet's career was typical of that of an engineer in pre-revolutionary France who did not receive formal training at the prestigious *Ecole des Ponts-et-Chaussees* but instead learnt his profession on the job. In the 27 years from 1748 to 1775 he went through all the ranks from an Under-Inspector to Inspector-General in the department of *Ponts-et-Chaussees*. Tresaguet began his real career as a highway engineer on 1 January 1748 when he was appointed under-engineer to the town of Moulins – the same place where his father had been engineer-in-chief until 1735. In the year 1764 he became an Engineer of the department of *Ponts-et-Chaussees* and chief engineer of the town of Limoges, and applied himself to the subject of road construction in the region. In 1775 Tresaguet produced his famous *Memorandum on the construction and maintenance of roadways* which became the subject of much interest and discussion by the department of *Ponts-et-Chaussees* before being distributed to all services of the department as a model document. By coincidence, in 1764 a system was introduced in France by his predecessor, Turgot, whereby the use of statutory labour (*la corvee*) for work on the roads was replaced by a tax, which allowed competent contractors to be employed instead of unskilled and often unwilling labour. Tresaguet was therefore able to make effective use of this new arrangement to carry out the construction of new stone roadways to his design. The later years of Tresaguet's career are not so well known. On his retirement, he was granted a pension and lived in a house in Paris that he had bought in 1788. The French revolution took place in 1789. Early in 1796 Tresaguet fell ill, and in March of the same year he died in his Paris house.

Tresaguet's Method of Road Construction

Before dealing with Tresaguet's method of road construction it is necessary to say a few words about units of length in pre-Revolutionary France. Before the Revolution, lengths in France were measured in *pied* (0.33 m) and *pouce* (2.7 cm). These old French units are close enough to the English foot (0.30 m) and inch (2.5 cm) respectively for the English terms to be used in the descriptions which follow without great loss of accuracy.

Tresaguet's method of road construction can be summarised in four stages. Firstly, to dig a trench so that the bottom profile of the trench is parallel to the future desired camber of the road surface, and to reduce the depth to 10 in instead of the 18 in used hitherto. Secondly, to lay the first layer of coarse stones edgewise instead of laying them flat in the bottom of the trench. Thirdly, to lay by hand a layer composed of successive applications of broken stone, well compacted so that there are no voids. Fourthly, to cover the whole with a layer 3 in thick consisting of stone broken by hand with a hammer into small pieces no bigger than a walnut (say 1.5 in).

A typical cross-section of a Tresaguet road is shown in Figure 6.1.

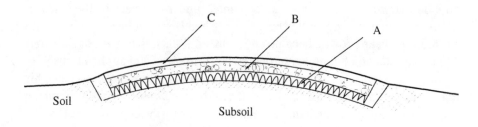

A: Stone hand pitching
B: Layer of coarser broken stone
C: 3 in thick layer of small broken stone

Figure 6.1   Cross-section of pavement structure of a Tresaguet road

Tresaguet stressed the following points. That the foundation should not be flat, that voids in the stone layers should be minimised, that the upper layer should be constructed with a high quality stone capable of forming a final crust on the surface, and that the completed road had to be maintained regularly to keep it in good condition. The cross sections of his roads show that the roads were provided with drainage ditches at either side and that the whole pavement was confined at its edges with large kerbstones. Finally, Tresaguet's pavement structure was only 10 in thick which offered a saving in material over the 18 in thick pavement that was commonly used before; this was claimed to be an important benefit.

If it is true that Tresaguet's pavement structure was only 10 in thick, this poses a problem that is difficult to resolve, which is that the thickness of the foundation layer of hand-pitching plus the intermediate layer of broken stone could only have been 7 in thick, because we know that the surface layer of small stones was 3 in thick. The thickness of 7 in seems to be insufficient for the combined foundation and intermediate layers, because hand-pitching by itself was usually about 6 in thick.

The width of the road depended upon its type, French roads in the eighteenth century being divided into four classes:

grandes routes (1st class) which were 60–42 ft wide;
grands chemins (2nd class) which were 48–36 ft wide;
chemins royaux (3rd class) which were 36–30 ft wide; and
chemins de traverse (4th class) which were 30–24 ft wide.

These widths must relate to the overall width between ditches and not to the width of the pavement. Tresaguet's cross sections of roads typically show 18 ft wide pavements with 12 ft wide verges on either side.

In spite of the warm reception of his *Memorandum*, the methods of Tresaguet were not very rapidly implemented throughout France; Paris and Limousin were the only regions that took up and practised his ideas. The disturbances of the Revolution and the Imperial wars that followed pushed Tresaguet's road construction ideas into the background until some 40 years later, in 1820, they were remembered and used again when the French road system was considerably extended.

However, an Englishman, Arthur Young, who was one of the last observers of life in rural France before the Revolution, made a journey across France and reported that some of the new roads in the Limoges region, namely those built by Tresaguet, were 'truly noble'. On his return to England, Young described these roads, so that the fame of Tresaguet's roads and, perhaps, knowledge of his methods may have spread to this country. But it is not known whether McAdam and Telford owe anything of their methods to a knowledge of Tresaguet's.

Phillips

Meanwhile, in Great Britain the problems of roadmaking and road maintenance were occupying the mind of Robert Phillips. In 1736 he presented a paper to the Royal Society entitled: *A dissertation concerning the present state of the high roads of England, especially those near London, wherein is proposed a new method of repairing and maintaining them*. His paper gave a full account of the bad practices then used, and indicated what should be done to improve things. His main concern was with the clay and gravel roads of southern England. He recognised the importance of good drainage, and observed that a properly prepared layer of gravel could be compacted by traffic into a firm surface. It is not known how influential Phillip's ideas were in terms of practical results, but we will now turn to three roadmakers who did have the most profound effect on British roads.

Metcalf

John Metcalf was born in 1717 at Knaresborough, Yorkshire into a poor family. When he was six years of age he caught smallpox, which left him blind. As a boy and young man, Metcalf did not allow his blindness to limit his activities, amongst which was that he learned to play the violin. He later turned this to advantage, earning a living by playing at social occasions in nearby Harrogate. Metcalf had a wide range of occupations, including running packhorses, but in 1765 he turned his mind to roadmaking. In that year, construction of a turnpike road between Harrogate and Boroughbridge had been authorised by Act of Parliament, and Metcalf offered to undertake the work. After this he went on to build roads all over Yorkshire, Lancashire and Cheshire, and during the next 30 years built more than 180 miles of turnpike roads. He retired from roadmaking in 1797 (aged 80!) and died in 1810

Metcalf's grasp of roadmaking is extraordinary given his disability, and that he had little education and could not, of course, read and write. Firstly, Metcalf insisted on good drainage, and designed the road to be 'crowned' so that it shed water to ditches that were provided on either side. Secondly, he understood the need for a proper road pavement which consisted of a foundation layer of large stones on top of which he placed excavated 'road material' (of now unknown composition) to raise the level of the road above that of the surrounding ground, followed by a layer of gravel to form the running surface. Thirdly, Metcalf insisted that the surfacing gravel must consist of angular particles which would knit together under the action of wagon and coach wheels, instead of round pebbles which would have been displaced easily by the wheels. Some elements of his road construction are very much like those of the Roman road and one wonders if, perhaps, someone had described a Roman road to him or whether he came to the design independently. Remarkably, Metcalf also built a road across a bog near Manchester on fascines, and built a highway bridge at Boroughbridge ('if the gentlemen would be kind enough to write the figures down' he would give them the dimensions of the span and abutments which he carried in his head).

McAdam

John Loudon McAdam was born in Ayr, Scotland on 21 September 1756. He was the youngest of the ten children of James McAdam and Susannah Cochrane (niece of the seventh Earl of Dundonald). In 1770, on the death of his father, McAdam went to New York where his uncle was already established as a merchant. By 1776 he was in business on his own account and in 1778 he married Glorianna Margaretta Nicoll, who possessed both beauty and fortune by contemporary accounts! In 1783 McAdam, his wife and their children returned to Scotland, and for the next 15 years McAdam managed his own estate and engaged in business including an association with Archibald Cochrane, ninth Earl of Dundonald, in one of Dundonald's firms the British Tar Company. In 1787 he became a trustee of the Ayrshire turnpike roads, thus kindling what was to become the main interest of his life – roadmaking – and the one that was to make his surname a household word. During the years between 1798 and 1814 he travelled extensively, observing the condition of roads wherever he went.

In 1801 McAdam settled in Bristol, and in due course was appointed a trustee of the Bristol Turnpike Trust; and in January 1816 was invited by his fellow trustees to become General Surveyor to the Trust. He was now in a position to put his theories into practice and soon the turnpike roads of the Bristol area were a model for the whole country. McAdam remained General Surveyor of the Bristol Trust until his death, but in addition to this post he went on to hold 17 other posts as Surveyor, as well as becoming a national authority on roadmaking, giving evidence to Select Committees of Parliament on several occasions. As well as McAdam himself, his sons and other members of his family became involved in the roadmaking business, no fewer than eight being employed by various turnpike trusts. In February 1825 McAdam's wife died and in 1827 he married her 40 year-old cousin Anne Charlotte De Lancey, McAdam then being 71. In the same year he moved from Bristol to Hoddesdon, Hertfordshire where Anne had a house. Thereafter McAdam lived at Hoddesdon, but each year he spent the summers in Scotland, returning south in the late autumn. It was on one of these visits to Scotland that he died at Moffat, Ayrshire on 26 November 1836.

McAdam's Views on Road Construction

By 1811 McAdam had crystallised his wide observations on the state of roads in Great Britain into two conclusions, the first identifying why the existing roads were so bad and the second defining how a good road should be made. He set down these conclusions for the benefit of a Select Committee as follows, somewhat abridged:

The observations I have made in a period of twenty-six years on the roads of this kingdom, and the opportunities I had of making comparisons of the different kinds of materials and modes of their application, have led me to form the following conclusions.

1st. That the present bad condition of the roads in the kingdom, is owing to the injudicious application of the materials with which they are repaired, and to the defective form of the roads.

2nd. That the introduction of a better system of making the surface of the roads, and the application of scientific principles, which has hitherto never been thought of, would remedy this evil.

The object to be attained in a good road, as far as regards the surface, is to have it smooth, hard, and so flat as that a carriage may stand quite upright.

A road made of small broken stone, without mixture of earth, of the depth of ten inches, will be smooth, hard and durable; this is proved by all experience: it seems only necessary therefore to enquire by what means this desirable object may be attained all over the kingdom.

As well as having strong views on road construction, McAdam had strong views on road vehicles. At the time, the various turnpike trusts charged different tolls for wagons having wheels of different widths, in order to encourage the use of wide wheels in the belief that the widest wheels did the least damage to the road. Heavy wagons could have wheels up to 16 in wide. However, wide-wheeled vehicles could only travel slowly, and this tendency therefore hindered the development of efficient vehicles for the transport of freight by road. McAdam argued that this was wrong and that 'instead of the vehicles being made to suit the roads, the roads should be made to suit the vehicles'. This principle laid down by McAdam has been accepted as an article of faith by road engineers ever since, and this point will be returned to later in this book.

Although McAdam claimed his method of road construction was based upon scientific principles, it was in fact based upon empirical observations on the effects of the existing traffic on the existing roads. McAdam noted that the contact area of a normal coach wheel on the road surface was about one inch square, and he said that because of this no piece of roadstone should be greater than one inch in size. The reason for this was that if the pieces of stone were larger than the contact area of the wheel, their size prevented them from being compacted by the wheels of the traffic to give the dense smooth surface required for a good road. McAdam observed that the large stones commonly used for roadmaking lay loose on the surface until the wheels of a passing coach either pushed them out of the way or bumped joltingly over them: whichever happened they were serving no useful purpose to the road, and in the latter case were positively injurious to the wheels of vehicles. Roadstone broken down into pieces about one inch in size came to be called *macadam*, and a road that had been improved by having been provided with a macadam pavement was referred to as having been *macadamised*. In this way McAdam's name entered common parlance.

McAdam's Road Structure

The cross section of the road pavement devised by McAdam is shown in Figure 6.2. The first step was to prepare the formation and dig drainage ditches along both sides. The formation was finished to a camber and on this was placed a layer of broken stone, the individual pieces of which were not more than one inch in diameter. The layer of stone was rammed flat with wooden pounders. On this was placed a carpet of finer stone which in course of time became cemented with stone dust. The stone dust itself was produced by the grinding action of the iron-tyred traffic running on the road, and rainfall washed the dust into the crevices between the stone particles binding them together. We know now that the cementing action derived from the surface tension of water in the dust (i.e. the suction), although contemporary opinion at the time considered that the stone dust itself was cementitious – limestone being particularly favoured for possessing this quality. The surface of the road was finished with a camber of 3 in rise at the centre of an 18 ft wide carriageway.

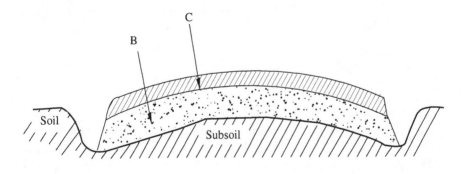

B: Layer of broken stone (1 in diameter pieces)
C: Carpet of finer stone cemented by stone powder and water

Figure 6.2 Cross section of pavement structure of a McAdam road

To begin with, McAdam liked to 'make a road in three times', by which he meant he liked to lay about 3 in of metalling at a time, allowing the traffic to compact each layer, with the ruts being raked smooth periodically. In this way three layers were laid, giving a finished road pavement some 9-10 in thick. However, after about 1820 road rollers came into use which made unnecessary the practice of allowing the traffic to do the compaction. Much of McAdam's work was in reconstructing existing roads as well as making new ones. When an existing road was to be 'macadamised' all the existing road material was lifted and moved to the side of the road. It was then sifted to remove earth and soil. The large stones were broken down to the standard one-inch size and used for the new road pavement, thereby saving the owners from the expense of purchasing new material. Although the heavy work was done by fit labourers, the task of stone-breaking was often carried out by women, children and unfit men, who would sit by the roadside, hammers in hands, producing steadily growing piles of small stones. These were checked periodically by surveyors who carried a spring balance to check that the stones were the regulation six ounces in weight – a stone of this weight being of the correct size (in point of fact a 6 oz. stone is about 1.5 in).

Stone-breaking by hand for road maintenance was still being done by women sitting by the roadside well into the twentieth century – as evidenced by oral testimony from the women involved, some of whom are still alive. The women, known as 'knappers' were issued with spectacle frames to which pieces of wire gauze were fitted in place of lenses in order to protect their eyes from flying chips of stone.

Telford

Thomas Telford was born in 1757 at Glendinning in Dumfries and Galloway, Scotland, the only child of an Eskdale shepherd and his wife. When he left school Telford was first an apprentice and then a journeyman stonemason at nearby Langholm. In 1782 he left Scotland for London where he soon got work as a mason on the new Somerset House. In 1784 Telford was superintending building works at Portsmouth dockyard, a job he probably owed to the patronage of William Pulteney for whom he had done some work previously. The work at Portsmouth finished in 1786, but in the meantime Pulteney had been elected Member of Parliament for Shrewsbury, and he immediately commissioned Telford to renovate the derelict Shrewsbury Castle so that he could occupy it. In 1787, again with Pulteney's influence, he secured the position of Surveyor of Public Works for the County of Shropshire, and this appointment marks the beginning of his career as a *civil engineer*, a profession of which he is considered to be the father in Great Britain. Telford went on to construct many great civil engineering works, notably canals and bridges, but it is his work on roads that concern us here. In 1801 Telford was asked to make proposals for improving the roads in the Scottish highlands, some of which had fallen into disrepair. His proposals were accepted and in 1803 he was authorised to carry them out, building some 920 miles of new roads, remaking and realigning 280 miles of the old military roads and building over 1,000 new bridges during the next 18 years. In 1815 Telford also commenced work on the Holyhead Road which is described below and which went on for 15 years. Because of these great works the poet Robert Southey dubbed Telford 'The Colossus of Roads'. In 1820, such was Telford's reputation that he was invited to become the first President of the newly formed Institution of Civil Engineers and in 1827 he was made a Fellow of the Royal Society. In 1828 the Institution was awarded its Royal Charter and by 1830 it was firmly established as the professional body for civil engineers and civil engineering. Telford died in 1834 and is buried in the nave of Westminster Abbey.

Telford's Road Structure

The cross section of a typical Telford road is shown in Figure 6.3. The first step was to excavate and prepare a level (i.e. not cambered) formation, and the drainage ditches on either side of the road. On the prepared formation was placed a 7 in thick layer of foundation stones which were hand-pitched on edge with the broad end of each stone downward; the upward pointing tips of the stones were then chipped off and the chips hammered down into the crevices between the stones to form a dense mass. Next, a layer of smaller stones, broken to not more than the size of a hen's egg, was laid and on some jobs Telford provided ring gauges of 2.5 in diameter for grading the maximum size of the stones used in this layer. This layer was 5 in thick at the edges and 7 in thick at the crown so as to provide the requisite camber, and it was sometimes placed in two layers. Finally, a 1.5 in layer of even finer broken stone or gravel was laid to form the road surface, giving a total pavement thickness of some 13.5–15.5 in. The action of the iron tyres running on the upper layer soon produced grit and dust which packed down between the stones and produced a smooth running surface. The final profile was finished to a camber of 2 in rise on an 18 ft wide carriageway.

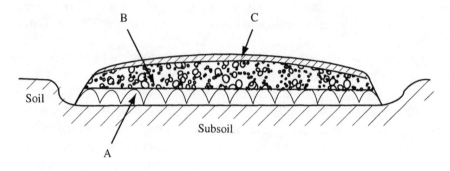

C: Layer of broken stone bound with fine material
B: Layer of broken stone
A: Stone hand-pitching with chips

Figure 6.3   Cross-section of pavement structure of a Telford road

Telford placed great emphasis on the proper grading of the stone for the different layers, and as we have seen he provided ring gauges for checking the maximum size (these may have looked like the ring gauge shown in Figure 7.6 in the next chapter). He also insisted on the importance of his foundation layer, which he claimed followed the example of the Romans, but which seems to derive more from his early experience as a stonemason. Macadam's roads did not have a foundation and Telford considered that his roads would in the long run prove more durable than Macadam's because of this.

The Holyhead Road

In 1798 a small French military expedition succeeded in landing in Ireland and this triggered an uprising against British rule. Although the incursion was promptly dealt with and the uprising was easily suppressed, the British Prime Minister, William Pitt the younger, decided that union of the two islands was the only way to restore order permanently in Ireland. Therefore, the Irish Parliament was abolished and from 1801 Ireland sent her representatives to the British Parliament at Westminster. In 1800 an Act for the Union of Great Britain and Ireland was passed and the cross of St Patrick was added to the national flag to give the familiar Union Flag that we now have today; the union was known as the United Kingdom. However, it was more easy to create a political union than a physical union as the Irish members of parliament found out when they had to travel to and fro from Ireland to Great Britain. The Post Office, responsible for communications between London and Dublin, were also concerned. The journey was made by road from London to Holyhead and then by packet to Dublin, and it was the Holyhead Road that was the problem. Seventeen turnpike trusts were responsible for the road from London to Shrewsbury and seven more for the road from Shrewsbury to Holyhead. The further west you went the worse the road became: London mail coaches could not go beyond Shrewsbury and in Anglesey there was hardly a road at all. The Postmaster General tried to get the Welsh turnpike trusts to put their roads in good order but it was completely beyond their means.

Eventually, due to the efforts of Sir Henry Parnell, a Holyhead Road Commission was set up in 1815 and instructed Telford to first survey the route, and then improve the existing road where possible, but construct where necessary a new road. Between London and Shrewsbury Telford worked with the existing turnpike trusts but the many improvements needed were constructed directly by the Commission and then handed over to the trusts to manage. Between Shrewsbury and Holyhead the existing turnpike trusts were taken over and this section of the road, nearly all new construction, became the direct responsibility of the Commission. The work went on for 15 years, although before it was finished mail coaches were able to run through to Holyhead. The time taken, and the cost, were in some measure due to the use of Telford's rather massive pavement structure – if Macadam's method had been used it would probably have been quicker and cheaper to build. However the Commissioners got a Rolls-Royce road for their money, and one that was greatly admired at the time. The Holyhead Road was made an astonishing 30 ft wide. It is now the A5.

Although outside the scope of this book, it is worth remarking that on the Holyhead Road Telford displayed an intuitive mastery of the subjects that were later to be known as soil mechanics and rock mechanics. Telford designed the road with a maximum gradient of 1 in 20, which in the mountains necessitated the construction of cuttings, embankments, revetments and retaining walls, together with their drainage works, as well as numerous bridges. Finally, to carry the Holyhead Road across the Menai Strait to Anglesey, in 1825 Telford built the Menai Suspension Bridge, one of his finest achievements, and a monumental work of civil engineering that is still in use today.

The Roadmakers Compared

It is instructive to compare the great eighteenth and nineteenth century roadmakers. Table 6.1 shows the periods when they were active.

Table 6.1   The roadmakers' important dates

Roadmaker	Date of birth	Period of activity as roadmaker		Date of death and age	
Tresaguet	1716	1748–86	38	1796	80
Metcalf	1717	1765–97	32	1810	93
McAdam	1756	1787–1827	40	1836	80
Telford	1757	1787–1821	34	1834	77

Table 6.1 shows that the roadmakers fell into two groups: Tresaguet and Metcalf being the forerunners, mainly completing their work before McAdam and Telford who followed. Having said this, there are a number of things that the roadmakers had in common: firstly, they all lived to an old age, and secondly, they all practised roadmaking for a long time. Although the sample is far too small to be statistically significant, it is interesting to note that practising the profession of roadmaking appears to be associated with a long period of productive activity and with longevity. The long lives of the four roadmakers is all the more remarkable considering that life expectancy in western Europe in 1830 was only 40 years. What is more certain is that their live's work was of much benefit to their fellow citizens, and left a tangible mark of improvement on the country.

The technical details of the roadmakers' pavement structures are summarised in Table 6.2.

Table 6.2   Technical details of the pavement structures

Detail	Tresaguet	Metcalf	McAdam	Telford
Surface profile	Cambered	Cambered	Cambered	Cambered
Side ditches	Yes	Yes	Yes	Yes
Main construction layer	Broken stone, max size 1.5 in	Broken stone?	Broken stone, max size 1 in	Broken stone, max size 2.5 in
Foundation	Hand pitching	Large stones	None	Hand pitching
Formation profile	Cambered	Not known	Cambered	Flat
Total pavement thickness	10 in	Not known	9–10 in	13.5–15.5 in

Table 6.2 shows that all the roadmakers understood the need for good drainage, providing both a cambered surface profile for the road and side drainage ditches. Some even provided a cambered formation to assist in draining any water that did pass through the pavement. They all used broken stone of small size for the main construction, thereby eliminating one of the evils of previous roads – large stones that could wreck coach wheels. They all provided a good thickness of pavement, Telford's being the thickest with its hand-pitched foundation.

Although the roadmakers all provided a cambered surface for their roads in order to shed rainwater, Tresaguet, McAdam and Telford took pains to stipulate that the camber should have only a low rise. The reason for this was to allow coaches to run easily and safely at the sides of the road rather than having to run on the crown of the road. In this way, they prevented the undesirable concentration of wear on the crown of the road that has been described at the end of chapter 4.

All these road pavement structures would have been liable to frost damage in the winter. Probably, by a process of trial and error, rocks would have been selected for roadstone that were not susceptible to frost shattering, but the pavements would have been susceptible to frost loosening and maintenance in the form of regrading and recompaction of the surface would have been necessary after the spring thaw. The pavement structures themselves would have not been susceptible to frost heave either, but we need to consider whether frost heave could have occurred in the subgrade. If we take a total thickness of construction of 10 in (250 mm) as in a McAdam road, this gives protection of the subgrade for winters with frost indices of up to $(250 \div 50)^2$, which is a frost index of 25. Comparing this value with Figure 1.5 shows that for much of Great Britain there would have been a likelihood of frost heave in the winter in road subgrades where the soil was frost-susceptible and the water table was high. However, a Telford road with its greater pavement thickness of 15 in (corresponding to a frost index of 56) would have offered much more frost protection to the subgrade.

The Problem of Dust

All these stone roads required some degree of attrition of the stone by coach wheels and horse hooves to produce grit and dust which was then washed down by rainwater into the interstices between the stones to bind the material together. (It will be recalled that coach wheels, although being made of wood had iron tyres, and that horses were shod with iron shoes.) Some rocks were better than others in this respect and, where available, the hard Carboniferous Limestone from the Pennines and the Mendips was much favoured by the roadmakers. Tresaguet also writes of the need for the stone to be of good quality and capable of forming a crust on the road surface. Flint, widespread in southern England, was probably the least suitable rock, being too hard to readily break down, and lacking cohesion even when it did; there is some evidence that when the only rock available was flint, a little silt and clay with it was necessary to give the degree of cohesion needed for a satisfactory road pavement.

However, this grit and dust that was so necessary was also a very great nuisance in the summer when the surface of the road became baked dry by the sun and the passage of horses and coaches whipped up great clouds of dust which smothered the travellers. This was a nuisance everywhere of course, but no more so than on the Bath Road (now the A4) which carried the fashionable members of London's high society to Bath, ostensibly to take the waters, but actually to take part in a regional variation of the social round. The road dust not only inconvenienced these prestigious travellers themselves, but – maybe more importantly – soiled their fine clothes and hats.

The dust problem was solved by no less a person than Beau Nash, the colourful director of social life at Bath. Nash commissioned the construction, at appropriate intervals along the Bath Road, of underground cisterns made of brick which during the winter stored water that flowed into them from the ground water table. Each cistern had fixed above it a cast-iron hand-operated pump by which the water could be pumped up to the surface. Local men were employed in the summer to douse the dust by sprinkling water on the road surface, using water pumped up from the cisterns for this purpose. This measure not only solved the problem of keeping the travellers free from the dust nuisance, but had the additional benefit of preventing the loss of the desirable fines from the road pavement. Some of these pumps can still be seen by the side of the A4 where they are preserved as attractive, historical pieces of roadside furniture.

The Turnpikes

The system of maintaining the roads by statute labour eventually came to be seen as completely inadequate for the upkeep of all but local roads at the parish level, and ways were sought replace statute labour with a more professional approach for highways. The system that was created to provide this was the turnpike system, whereby a trust was set up by influential residents in the area (the trustees) which undertook to repair and maintain in good condition a section of road in return for the right to levy tolls on travellers. The word *turnpike* derives from the gates topped with pikes fixed across the road at intervals at the location where the tolls had to be paid. Parliamentary turnpike trust Acts date from 1706, and gradually the system replaced statute labour and tollgates became a familiar, if unpopular, sight to travellers on English highways.

By the end of the 1730s a striking change was being brought to British roads by the introduction of turnpike trusts. Before 1730 there were only a few turnpike trusts. Main roads, including much of the Great North Road and almost all the Great West Road depended on the statute labour of the unfortunate parishes through which they passed for their upkeep and maintenance. There is much evidence, some of which we have seen in chapter 4, that the main roads of England in early Georgian times (say 1715–30) were a national disgrace. Turnpike trusts were a means whereby substantial sums of locally raised capital could be injected into the construction, rehabilitation, repair and maintenance of roads; return on the capital so invested was guaranteed by the revenue from the graduated system of tolls levied on the passing traffic. The golden age of the turnpikes was the four middle decades of the eighteenth century. A large proportion of the new roads constructed by the turnpike trusts was in the north of England and the west Midlands. In 1840 it is estimated that there were about 22,000 miles of turnpike road in Great Britain, and by 1770 the turnpikes provided a genuinely national system of road transport (Figure 6.4). York, Manchester and Exeter were three days' travel in 1720 but by 1780 they were only 24 hours away. The turnpikes were to be taken to perfection in the 1820s with the work of MacAdam and Telford. During the same period, the paving of city streets was greatly improved, commencing with the work of the Westminster Paving Commissioners in 1762.

The first turnpike trusts, for all their good intentions, had little idea of how to build roads. A common method was to dig a ditch on either side of the road, pile the earth from the ditches into the centre and cover it with a thin layer of gravel. This probably served during the first summer but became a quagmire in the winter. The turnpike trusts also tried to regulate the traffic using the roads: believing that wheels with narrow rims damaged the road, the trusts tried to stipulate that wagon wheels should have rims of 9, 13 and 16 in width so that they would not produce ruts but instead help to roll the surface flat. This was trying to suit the traffic to the road and in the end was

Figure 6.4   Turnpike roads in 1770

unsuccessful. Also, because it was considered that heavy vehicles damaged the road more than light vehicles, the turnpike trustees were empowered to charge tolls that increased with the weight of the vehicle. The main turnpike roads had elaborate weighing engines, which actually raised coaches and waggons right off the ground in order to weigh them, so that the correct toll could be levied. To begin with, many trusts were reluctant to appoint civil engineers to the position of Surveyor, but once McAdam had demonstrated so strikingly how the roads of the Bristol area could be improved this antipathy declined and many of the trusts adopted his methods.

It is important to note that the turnpike roads were principally intended for coach traffic. Most heavy freight and bulk commodities such as coal and building stone were carried by barge on canals and inland waterways, or by coastwise shipping of which there was a thriving trade.

Most of the trusts eventually used McAdam's method of roadmaking rather than Telford's, and the reasons for this are as follows. Firstly, McAdam's road structure did not have the stone foundation that Telford's had and was therefore cheaper to construct – a factor that appealed to the trusts. Secondly, many of the turnpikes were reconstructed roads rather than completely new roads, and McAdam's method lent itself to the remaking of the road because the stone from the existing road could be lifted, cleaned and then broken to provide macadam for the new pavement. Thirdly, Telford was a civil engineer who practised principally in other fields of the profession as well as roadmaking, while McAdam was solely a road engineer who could devote all his attention to promoting and practising his method.

The coming of the railways in the 1830s increasingly took traffic from the roads and this led to the decline of the turnpike system. As far as tolls were concerned the heyday of the trusts was 1837, the most profitable year, but by 1850 receipts had begun to fall sharply. From the 1860s onwards both the trusts and the coaching industry found it difficult to compete with the railways and an increasing number of roads became 'disturnpiked'. Finally, in 1888 the Local Government Act set up the county councils with responsibility for all main roads in their counties. The last toll on a genuine turnpike trust road was collected on 1 November 1895 on the Anglesey section of Telford's Holyhead Road.

In recent times there has been a resurrection in the use of macadam for drives and paths subject to heavy pedestrian, or light vehicular, traffic in historic country houses and parks where the use of a concrete or bituminous surfacing would be out of place. In the proper setting, these macadam drives give a very good impression (including in summer the dust!) of what an eighteenth-century macadamised road was like. Also, there is a reconstruction of a turnpike road, complete with tollgate and tollkeeper's house, at the Blist's Hill Open Air Museum, Ironbridge, Shropshire.

The Steamroller

The Frenchman, Nicolas-Joseph Cugnot, is credited with the invention of the first steam-driven vehicle to run on ordinary roads in 1769, and this was followed in Great Britain by the Cornish engineer, Richard Trevithick's well-known steam carriage of 1801. Between 1820 and 1860 many attempts were made to introduce steam-driven carriages and lorries, including the notable vehicles of Sir Goldsworthy Gurney, but in the event, steam locomotion found its successful application on the railways rather than on the roads. Of more importance to the subject of this book – road construction – was the use of steam to power the steamroller.

During the 1830s the practice had been introduced of compacting macadam during construction using light, horse-drawn iron rollers rather than waiting for the traffic to compact the road pavement. In France, where macadamised roads were adopted in about 1830 and the horse-drawn roller was introduced in 1833, it was said that 'a road unrolled is only half finished'. The main drawback of the horse-drawn road roller was that it was not heavy enough to be effective. The application of steam power to this purpose did not happen until 1859 when the first steamroller was invented in France. Several French models followed but it was not until 1866 that steamrollers were made in England (by Aveling and Porter). The success of the steamroller was due to its steam engine which was powerful enough to propel a vehicle that was sufficiently heavy to be an effective road roller. It is not an exaggeration to say that the steamroller gave the macadamised road a new lease of life. It was heavy enough, and powerful enough, to compact macadam to a dense state that made for a strong, durable pavement. Also, instead of waiting for the traffic to produce fines, these were now added to the macadam as it was laid, together with just enough water to assist compaction and give cohesion to the stone. Not only did the steamroller transform the laying of new macadamised roads, but it was a boon to the maintenance of existing ones. Potholes could be filled in with compacted stone rather than loose stone, and the surface could be relaid and rolled to a smooth finish without waiting for the traffic to do the job. Individual steamrollers often had long lives – more than 50 years – and were cared for lovingly by the successive drivers through whose hands they passed.

* * *

In 1870 the President of the Institution of Civil Engineers, Charles Blacker Vignoles, compiled a Table giving the lengths of good, carriageable, stone-paved roads in Europe. It is shown here as Table 6.3.

Table 6.3   Lengths of stone-paved roads in 1868–69

Country	Length of road (miles)	Area (square miles)	Population
United Kingdom	160,000	122,519	30,621,431
France	100,048	210,460	38,192,064
Prussia	55,818	139,675	23,970,641
Spain	10,886	198,061	15,673,481

The table shows two things: firstly, that the United Kingdom had the largest network in spite of having the smallest area; and secondly, that the idea of stone-paved roads had spread from France and the United Kingdom to other countries in Europe. Both these were a matter of some pride to British civil engineers. There is some irony in Vignoles' endorsement of British road construction because he was predominantly a railway engineer and, therefore, in those days, a rival of the road engineer!

Finally, a military note. During the Revolutionary and Napoleonic Wars (1793–1815), when Great Britain was at war with France, numerous defensive measures were taken to protect the country from invasion. In particular, in 1804, when Napoleon amassed a large army together with a huge flotilla at Boulogne, some 400,000 volunteers responded to a call to defend the island. The official proclamation called for three classes of volunteer: volunteers bearing arms, pioneers and labourers, and drivers of wagons. The proclamation defined the duties of the second group, who were to provide themselves with pickaxes spades and shovels, as follows: 'As pioneers and labourers you will be employed in breaking up roads to hinder the enemy's advance.' This contingency showed a lively recognition that roads could well assist an invading force should the defending force prove to be inadequate.

7   The Coming of the Motor Car

They saw a small cloud of dust,
with a dark centre of energy,
advancing on them at incredible speed.

The end of the nineteenth century saw Great Britain provided with a network of macadamised roads inherited mainly from the turnpike trusts. But this network was no longer the primary transport system of the country, that role having been taken over by the railways for goods, freight, mail and fast passenger journeys. However, as the twentieth century began the beginning of another change was already apparent – the advent of the motor car – but before discussing its effects we must make brief mention of the bicycle.

The introduction of the pneumatic tyre in 1888 made the bicycle a practical proposition and in 1890–95 there was a cycling boom. However, increasing use of bicycles showed that they were unsuited to macadamised roads, for not only did bicycle tyres get punctured frequently by the stones in the surface, but the pneumatic tyres themselves loosened stones by a sort of suction action as they rolled over the road surface. So road engineers had forewarning that the macadamised road was no longer suited to the traffic.

The first motor cars, powered by the petrol-fuelled internal-combustion engine, were introduced into England from France in about 1895, but these early models had wheels that were fitted with solid rubber tyres. By 1903, when motor car speeds had risen to 20 miles per hour, pneumatic tyres had become necessary in order to give a satisfactory ride, and they soon became standard. In the succeeding years, the increasing number of pneumatic-tyred motor cars compounded by many times the problems of punctures and the plucking out of stones from the road surface that had first been brought to light by the bicycle. Also, in the summer the pneumatic tyres sucked up great clouds of dust from the road surface that made the wearing of goggles by motorists universal, as shown by contemporary photographs and prints.

The first solution to the dust problem was to emulate Beau Nash and try to damp down the dust with water. At the turn of the century horse-drawn water carts, equipped with perforated sprinkler bars were a familiar sight on

72

the roads in the summer as they trundled up and down 'laying the dust'.

However, a more permanent solution to these problems was required and one approach lay in finding a means to bind the stones in road surface together and seal the surface against the suction action of the pneumatic tyres.

Tarmacadam

The discovery of a solution to these problems was a remarkable example of what has been called 'accidental innovation', that is one that is made as a result of an accident or chance occurrence. In 1901 E. Purnell Hooley, the county surveyor of Nottingham, in the course of a visit to the Denby Ironworks, noticed a length of dust-free road. On enquiry he was told that a barrel of tar had burst at that spot and a pool of tar had spread along the road; the pool of tar had then been covered with ironworks slag in order to mop it up, and the resulting mixture had formed the dust-free surface he had admired. Inspired by this, Hooley experimented with mixtures of slag aggregate and coal tar, and in 1902 patented the material which was called *tarmacadam* to distinguish it from ordinary macadam. Tarmacadam can, of course, be made using crushed rock aggregate as well as slag, and tarmacadam became one of the standard twentieth century materials for constructing dust-free motor roads. Coal tar was a by-product of the coal gas industry and was readily available in the days when every city and town had a gas works. However, in the 1970s, coal tar ceased to be available because of the change from coal gas to natural gas and the demise of gas works, so that tarmacadam could no longer be made using tar as the binder. A substitute was soon found in bitumen, a by-product of the petroleum industry (see below), and tarmacadam continued to be made, although it was now called *bitumen macadam* instead of tarmacadam.

As well as providing a dust-free and stable road surface, tarmacadam also had one further great advantage – it was impermeable and thus prevented rainwater from entering the road structure. Impermeability was also a property of surface dressing and asphalt, two other bituminous road materials, to be described below.

Ordinary macadam still continued, and indeed continues, to be used, but as a roadbase material rather than a road surfacing material. For this use, a graded, crushed-rock aggregate is mixed with just sufficient water to confer some cohesion to the mass, and the mixture is known as *waterbound macadam* or *wetmix*. Wetmix provides a satisfactory roadbase, except for heavily trafficked roads, provided it is covered with an adequate thickness of bituminous surfacing. The first stone-crusher was constructed as early as 1858 for use in providing macadam for New York, but in Great Britain stone breaking by large gangs of men using hand-held hammers continued to be practised until well into the twentieth century. However, by 1920 portable mechanical stone-crushers were being introduced into the quarries, supplanted stone-knapping by hand.

The word *tarmac*, derived by shortening *tarmacadam*, is used today in a loose way to denote any road surface of a bituminous nature, although highway engineers often use *blacktop* instead as a generic term for bituminous road surfaces. The ordinary public also uses *tarmac* to denote airfield runway surfaces although many of these are in fact of concrete.

Surface Dressing

Tarmacadam was a replacement for ordinary macadam and was used primarily in the construction of new roads. For the existing network of macadamised roads a slightly different approach, also using coal tar, was used which came to be known as *surface dressing*. Coal tar was delivered from the gas works to the roadside in barrels and then heated in horse-drawn coal-fired tar boilers. The molten tar was then tapped off as required and poured on the macadam road surface from buckets or watering cans and brushed out over the surface by hand. The tarred surface was then blinded by 0.75 in or 0.5 in stone chippings, followed by 0.25 in chippings which were racked in between the coarser chippings. Finally, the surface was rolled with a steamroller to embed the chippings and give a smooth finish. Many of the existing macadamised roads of the nineteenth century were brought up-to-date during the early twentieth century by successive layers of surface dressing, which over a period of time provided an impermeable surfacing, thereby relegating the original macadam to the role of a roadbase. As for tarmacadam, when coal tar became unavailable for surface dressing, it was replaced by bitumen. It is interesting to note that many of the lay-bys on our present-day roads have their origins in the temporary storage areas that were used to stockpile chippings by the side of the road for surface dressing operations.

Asphalt

Asphalt is a naturally occurring bituminous material to which, for road construction purposes, is added natural sand or sand-sized powdered limestone particles. Asphalt was discovered in the nineteenth century at a number of localities, notably at the famous Trinidad Pitch Lake in the island of Trinidad in the West Indies, and at Seyssel near Lake Annecy in France. The first commercial shipment of Trinidad asphalt came to Great Britain in about 1840. *Rock asphalt* is limestone naturally impregnated with asphalt which only had to be crushed to produce a suitable road construction material. Asphalt was applied by heating to 150–200°C and then spreading on the road while hot. Natural rock asphalts usually contain about 80–90 per cent rock. The natural rock asphalts used in Great Britain that were imported from France (Gard region) and Switzerland (Val de Travers region) contained about 90 per cent rock.

Rock asphalt was used from 1835 for road construction in France on a limited scale and was first used on the streets of Paris in 1854; it was introduced into London for use on some of the city streets in 1869. It proved to a very hard-wearing surface for city roads and streets, but at first did not find much application on highways, probably because it was in competition with the less expensive, and more widely available, tarmacadam. Later, as happened with tarmacadam, asphalt was manufactured using bitumen as the binder. At the end of the nineteenth century an American, Clifford Richardson, inspected and analysed successful asphalt pavements from all over the United States and Europe. He found that as well as mixes of natural asphalt, there were also mixes of natural sand with bitumen or tar as the binder. Richardson wrote a book entitled *Modern Asphalt Technology* which ran to three editions and was hugely influential. As a result, in the early 1900s Richardson's findings were taken up and applied by British asphalt paving contractors. As a consequence, asphalt soon found wide application as surfacing on heavily trafficked roads where durability and resistance to deformation are required.

Refinery Bitumen

Bitumens artificially produced by the refining of crude petroleum are known as *refinery bitumens*, or more simply as *bitumens*, and an artificial rock asphalt can be made by mixing a suitably graded crushed rock aggregate with refinery bitumen. We have already noted that the substitution of refinery bitumen for tar gave rise to bitumen macadam in place of tarmacadam. Blends of natural asphalt and refinery bitumen are also used as bituminous binders for road materials.

As the petroleum industry grew in importance during the twentieth century, so refinery bitumen grew in importance for road construction. By 1936 about 85 per cent of the world's supply of asphalt was produced using refinery bitumen. The naturally occurring asphalts from Trinidad Lake and Val de Travers had a reputation of excellence as road materials that refinery bitumen had to compete with, not always easily. For example, in 1898 Mr Boulnois, the City Engineer of Liverpool complained that 'Dishonest contractors sometimes substitute inferior materials for natural asphalt – such imitation being made of ground chalk, fireclay and pitch or gas or ground limestone mixed with bitumen'. In view of this remark it is ironic that ground limestone mixed with bitumen was later to be one of the accepted recipes for artificial asphalt.

One reason for the continued popularity of Trinidad Lake asphalt, particularly for the wearing course of the surfacing, was the superior skidding resistance of natural asphalt, even though it was more expensive, compared with artificial asphalt made with refinery bitumen. A common compromise practice was to use a 50:50 mixture of natural asphalt and refinery bitumen because this was found to have reasonably good skidding resistance properties. The superior skidding resistance of natural asphalt was attributed to its faster rate of oxidation and the gritty nature of the oxidised material. Later on, chippings coated with bitumen and rolled in to the surface of the asphalt while it was still hot, were used to provide the required skidding resistance, and this practice finally overcame the last objection to the use of asphalt made with refinery bitumen.

Road materials used in the construction of modern bituminous pavements are described in more detail in Appendix 3.

* * *

The motor car is an example of what has been called 'composite innovation', namely an innovation that results from the bringing together of two or more elements to form a combination that is much more than the sum of the components. In this case the elements were the petrol engine and the pneumatic tyre; the motor car was of far greater importance than either of these. But there is another combination that is equally important and this is the combination of the motor car and the bituminously surfaced road. If no solution had been found to the problems the motor car encountered on trying to run on waterbound macadam roads, it is likely that the motor car would have remained of minor importance – probably restricted to operating on city streets. It is the bituminously surfaced road that allowed the motor car, and later the motor lorry, to develop to their present state of dominance in the national transportation system of the country.

Traditionally, since the earliest days of wheeled vehicles, the main operational properties required of a road have been that it should have a smooth, hard and durable surface. However, with the advent of fast motor vehicles with rubber tyres running on bituminously surfaced roads there arose the requirement for another important property – the need for the surface to have a high resistance to skidding – and from the 1950s efforts were made to provide this. The subject of skidding resistance is outside the main scope of this book, but for the interested reader a brief technical account is given in Appendix 4.

Concrete

The perceptive reader will have noted that waterbound macadam was concrete without the cement. Joseph Aspdin rediscovered how to manufacture Portland cement in 1824 and this led to the commencement of the use of concrete as a building and constructional material. However, it would seem that it was not applied to road construction in spite of the obvious nature of the application. At any time after say 1870 when steamrollers came into general use, it would have been a simple matter to add cement to waterbound macadam and produce a rolled-concrete road instead of a macadamised one. And yet this was not done – or at any rate, except for the instances mentioned below, not on any large scale – and thus remains one of the might-have-beens of the history of roads.

It will be recalled from chapter 3 that the Romans sometimes used concrete in their road pavements (see Figure 3.4a). Apart from this early use, the first concrete roads in Great Britain were constructed in Inverness and Edinburgh, Scotland, in 1865–66; the concrete was laid fairly dry and compacted and finished by roller, and these pavements performed satisfactorily until 1875. In the early years of the twentieth century experimental lengths of concrete pavement were constructed by county engineers and Port of London Authority engineers. In the United States the first concrete road pavement was laid at Bellefontaine, Ohio in 1893. This was followed in 1909 by a concrete highway built in Wayne County, Michigan; and another in 1912 at Saltney in Chester City, Ohio. However, by 1920, concrete pavements were being laid in the United States at the rate of 2,000 miles per year, and it was thought that this form of construction would be suitable for use in southern England where sand and gravel aggregates were available. As a result a number of bypasses on main roads were constructed in concrete. The service experience of these cannot have been wholly satisfactory because when the motorway network was designed and constructed in the 1950s–60s the Ministry of Transport did not normally allow concrete surfaced roads to be built. However, during this period the Road Research Laboratory carried out a number of full-scale concrete road experiments which resulted in renewed interest in concrete roads. The concrete industry made successful representations against the Ministry's policy, and since 1969 contractors have been allowed to use either concrete or bituminous construction for the Department of Transport's trunk roads and motorways.

The thickness of the slab of a concrete road pavement depended on whether it was reinforced or not and on the traffic loading, but for an unreinforced slab it varied from 230 mm for light traffic to 330 mm for heavy traffic. A typical road-slab concrete would have had mix proportions of 1:2:4 (1 part cement: 2 parts fine aggregate: 4 parts coarse aggregate), a water:cement ratio of 0.5:1 and a 28-day compressive strength of about 35 MN/m^2.

The proportions, together with corresponding lengths, of concrete roads in the United Kingdom, as estimated in 1986, are given in Table 7.1.

Table 7.1   Concrete roads in the United Kingdom

Category of road	Proportion %	Length km
All roads	5	17,500
All trunk roads and motorways	20	3,000
Trunk roads and motorways constructed since 1969	22	530
M25 motorway (see chapter 8)	46	90

It can be seen that the minority of British motorways and trunk roads have concrete pavements, which is in contrast to the situation in the United States where 53 per cent of interstate roads are of concrete.

In July 1992, following concern about the high level of noise generated by vehicle tyres running on concrete road surfaces, the Department of Transport once again imposed a ban on new concrete-surfaced construction for heavily trafficked motorways and trunk roads, although it still allowed concrete roadbase to be used with an asphalt surfacing.

Concrete roads were traditionally textured by brushing the surface before the concrete had hardened, the texture being provided to give the concrete surface the required skid resistance. It was this regular texture pattern that gave rise to the objectionable tyre noise. In 1993, in an attempt to solve the noise problem, concrete surfacing with a randomised surface texture pattern was produced by exposing the aggregate in the surface before the concrete had hardened. This had the effect of providing skid resistance without the undesired tyre noise. The material was called *exposed-aggregate concrete*. Although satisfactory, it was not as quiet a road surface as pervious macadam (see below). The places where exposed aggregate concrete has been laid on British roads were: M18 Yorkshire, and A50 Derbyshire. In 1996 the Department of Transport announced that exposed-aggregate concrete would be an allowable option for new road construction.

Road materials used in the construction of modern concrete pavements are described in Appendix 3.

* * *

During the Great War, 1914–18, all the main belligerent nations used the railways to transport both troops and war materials to the battlefields, so much so that the Great War has been described as having been conducted to the railway timetable. However, on the Western Front, over 1,000 London buses (and their drivers) were used to carry troops up to the front line – thereby being one of the first examples of motorised infantry. And in 1916 the French supplied the beleaguered fortress of Verdun by lorry. Also, during the Great War the appearance of the armoured car and the tank finally emphasised the importance of vehicles powered by the internal combustion engine.

In Great Britain after the Great War, there was a rapid growth in the use of motor transport for commercial and personal purposes, and the need for the government to take a greater interest in the national network of main roads became apparent. Accordingly, in 1919, the Ministry of Transport was established with responsibility for an integrated transport plan and for new roads. To begin with, and for some time afterwards, the Ministry operated through the existing county councils, using the county councils as its agents for carrying out work on the trunk roads in the various counties. The Ministry of Transport continued to be the responsible authority for trunk roads, including motorways when they came to be built, until the present day, except that it was later known as the Department of Transport.

In 1931 the Ministry of Transport set up a small experimental station at Harmondsworth, Middlesex, and in 1933 this was formally established as the Road Research Laboratory. It is from this date that the systematic application of science to road design and construction commenced in Great Britain. To begin with the subjects studied were soils, concrete and bituminous materials, together with skidding resistance and riding quality; later on studies of traffic and safety were added. The Laboratory, with two changes of name and one change of site, has continued in being until the present day, although in 1996 it was privatised under its present name: the Transport Research Laboratory. One of the principal subjects of research at the Laboratory, commencing in the late 1940s, was to devise a method for the design of road pavements; this research culminated in the publication of *Road Note No. 29: A guide to the structural design of flexible and rigid pavements for new roads* in 1960, and which subsequently went through two further editions (1965, 1970). The method by which road pavements were designed in the early 1960s will now be described and discussed.

Pavement Design

It is not known how the eighteenth and nineteenth century roadmakers decided on the thickness of their road pavement structures, but it was probably an empirical method based on trial-and-error combined with observation. There were not large differences in their final pavement thicknesses (10–15.5 in) as shown by Table 6.2 in chapter 6. As far as we know, these pavements were constructed of the same thickness irrespective of the nature of the underlying soils or of the intensity of the traffic.

In the early years of the twentieth century, some more enlightened city and county engineers carried out experiments with different kinds and thicknesses of road materials, and observed the deformations caused by traffic, but the information obtained was largely empirical and therefore of limited value because materials and methods of construction were changing and there was a growth in road traffic. What was needed was a more systematic approach that could be applied to different materials and different levels of traffic.

With the modern method of pavement design that was developed, two things had to be determined, namely the composition and the thickness of the pavement, and these, in turn, were dependent on the intended numbers of vehicles and their loading that the road was to carry and on the bearing capacity of the subgrade.

Traffic Classification

It will be recalled that the turnpike trustees considered that heavy vehicles damaged the road more than light vehicles and they levied their tolls accordingly. Modern research has confirmed this belief. Research carried out in the United States in the 1950s indicated that the damage caused to the road varied as the fourth power of the wheel load of the vehicle. To illustrate this let us compare the damaging effect of a four-wheel car having a mass of one ton with that of an 18-wheel articulated lorry having a mass of 36 tons. The wheel load of the car is 0.25 tonf and therefore the damaging effect of one wheel is 0.25^4. But because there are four wheels the damaging effect of the car is 4×0.25^4 which is $4 \times 0.004 = 0.016$. Turning now to the lorry, the wheel load is 2.0 tonf and therefore the damaging effect of one wheel is 2.0^4, and the damaging effect of the lorry as a whole is 18×2.0^4 which is $18 \times 16 = 288$. The damaging effect of the lorry divided by the damaging effect of the car is therefore $288 \div 0.016 = 18{,}000$. Put in simple terms, this means that the passage of one heavy lorry is as damaging to the road as the passage of 18,000 cars. This calculation shows that for roads carrying a mixed traffic of cars and lorries, the cars can be disregarded for pavement design purposes – all we need to know is how many lorries the road is expected to carry. Using this principle, traffic intensity was classified by the number of commercial vehicles per day in both directions that the road was expected to carry 20 years hence, using an annual rate of increase in traffic of 4 per cent. Commercial vehicles were defined as goods vehicles or public service vehicles having a mass of over 30 cwt when unladen. This traffic classification was as shown in Table 7.2.

Table 7.2   Traffic classification for pavement design purposes

Traffic class	Number of commercial vehicles per day	Design Chart No.
Light	150–450	4
Medium	450–1,500	3
Heavy	1,500-4,500	2
Very heavy and all motorways	more than 4,500	1

This traffic classification was later (after 1970) superseded by one based upon the cumulative axle load of vehicles.

Bearing Capacity of Subgrade

The bearing capacity of the subgrade of an intended road was measured by carrying out a test known as the *California bearing ratio* test, named after the California State highways department whose engineers developed it in 1929. To conduct the test, some soil from the proposed road line was compacted into a 6 in diameter, 5 in deep, mould to the same density and at the same moisture content as anticipated in the subgrade, and a 2 in diameter cylindrical plunger was slowly forced into the soil until it has penetrated to a depth of 0.3 in. Figure 7.1 shows the test apparatus. A curve of load against penetration was plotted on a standard chart as shown in Figure 7.2. The loads to produce penetrations of 0.1 in and 0.2 in were then expressed as a percentage of the loads to produce the same penetrations in a sample of standard crushed rock, and the higher of these numbers was the California bearing ratio of the soil. In practice, by comparison with the curves printed on it, the California bearing ratio of the soil under test was read directly off the chart as shown in Figure 7.2. Before the penetration was commenced, brass surcharge rings were usually placed on the surface of the soil to simulate the load of the pavement (these are not shown in Figure 7.1). Typical ranges of value of California bearing ratio for different soils are:

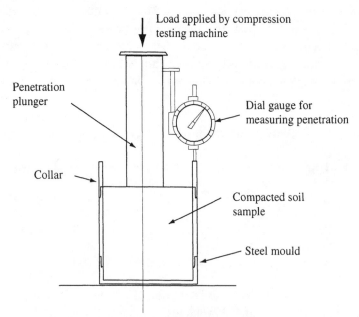

Figure 7.1   Apparatus for California bearing ratio test

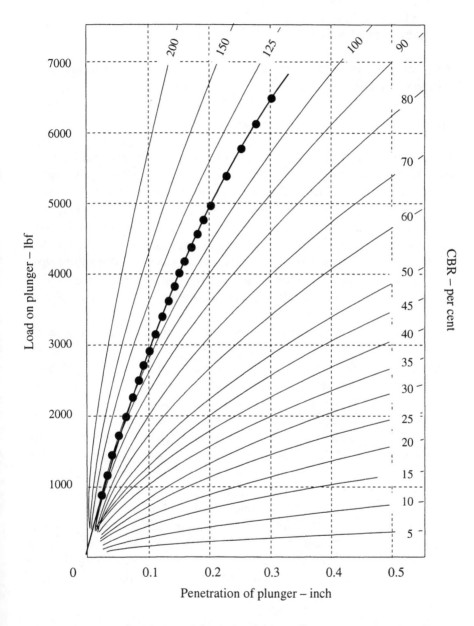

Figure 7.2 California bearing ratio chart with test result for hoggin. The California bearing ratio is 112 per cent

clays: 2–10 per cent;
sands: 15–50 per cent;
gravels: 50–100; and
hoggins: more than 100 per cent.

There was also a variant of the California bearing ratio test in which the subgrade was tested *in situ*.

Worked Example of Pavement Design

To illustrate the method of pavement design, we will imagine that in 1962 a road was to be designed to carry heavy traffic of 3500 commercial vehicles per day. Reference to Table 7.2 shows that Design Chart 2 has to be used. A California bearing ratio test has shown the heavy clay subgrade on the site has a value of 3 per cent. Using Design Chart 2, reproduced here as Figure 7.3, we see that a California bearing ratio of 3 per cent gives a thickness of sub-base of 13 in. The design chart also shows that on top of this sub-base we require a roadbase 8 in thick followed by 4 in of bituminous surfacing laid in two courses. This gives a total thickness of pavement construction of 25 in, of which the surfacing plus roadbase comprise 12 in.

Having found the thicknesses of the different layers of the pavement, the materials to be used must now be chosen. *Road Note No. 29* specifies the materials for surfacing to be used in conjunction with Design Chart 2 as shown here in Figure 7.4, which is an extract from a larger table. Because 3,500 commercial vehicles per day is in the upper part of the range, both the wearing course and the base course of the surfacing will be rolled asphalt. For the roadbase we have a choice from bitumen macadam, lean concrete or wetmix, and again because of the heavy traffic, bitumen macadam will be selected. For the sub-base, we require a material with a California bearing ratio of 15 per cent or more and we have a wide choice from crushed rock, natural gravel and sand, crushed slag, crushed-concrete hardcore or hoggin; we have available a frost-resistant hoggin with a California bearing ratio of 112 per cent (see Figure 7.2) which will be used. The result of the worked example of pavement design is shown in Figure 7.5. This example has been for a flexible pavement, but the method of design for rigid pavements followed similar principles.

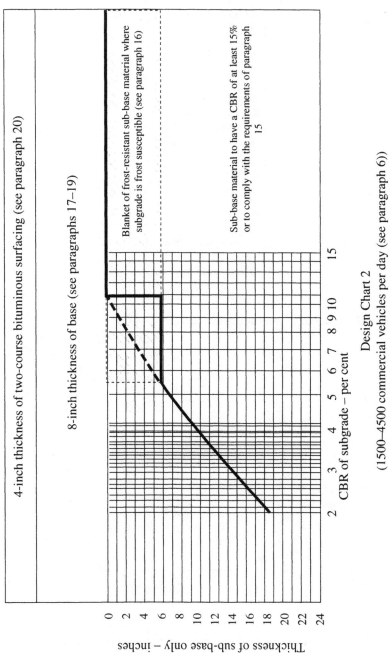

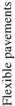

Figure 7.3 Example of pavement design chart. The 'paragraphs' refer to those in Road Note No. 29

Recommended bituminous surfacings for newly constructed roads

Design chart 2 (1500–4500 commercial vehicles per day)
1.5 in.   2.5 in.   4 in.

Wearing course
 Rolled asphalt –
   B.S.594
 Dense tar surfacing –
   B.R.T.A.
   specification
 	
 Base-course
 Rolled asphalt –
   B.S.594
 Close-textured bitumen
   macadam or
   tarmacadam
   (see Appendix 4)

Figure 7.4   Choice of surfacing material

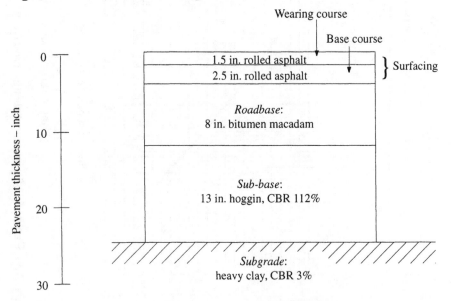

Figure 7.5   Result of worked example of pavement design

Alconbury Hill Experiment

In 1957 the Road Research Laboratory conducted a full-scale pavement design experiment on a section of dualling on the Great North Road, A1, at Alconbury Hill, Huntingdonshire. The experiment consisted of the construction of two experimental pavements, each 26 ft wide, one of flexible construction 1.5 miles long, and the other of rigid construction 1 mile long. The geological formations over the site were Oxford Clay, overlain in places by up to five feet of glacial boulder clay that was largely reworked and weathered Oxford Clay. These gave rise to a subgrade on the site consisting of heavy clay having a California bearing ratio of 5–9 per cent at the time of construction; but for the purposes of designing the pavements the California bearing ratio was assumed to be 3–5 per cent, this being the equilibrium that was estimated would be reached beneath the road after it was built. The traffic, estimated in 1957, was about 3,000 commercial vehicles per day, therefore falling within the 'heavy' traffic category of Table 7.2. The experimental pavements were constructed during the fine summer of 1957, and the road was opened to traffic in November of that year. The main purpose of the experiment was to test the validity of the pavement design methods that were subsequently issued as *Road Note No. 29*.

The main variables studied in the section of flexible pavement were the thickness and type of five different roadbase materials, and the thickness of the fine sand sub-base used throughout. The surfacing was mainly of rolled asphalt, but included short lengths of bitumen macadam. The main conclusions after six years of traffic (4,000 commercial vehicles per day) was that the thickness of roadbase and surfacing, and the types of materials used in these layers influenced the performance of the pavement much more than the overall thickness of construction. As might have been expected, rolled asphalt performed particularly well both as a surfacing and as a roadbase.

The main variables studied in the section of rigid pavement were the thickness of slab, the thickness and type of two different sub-bases, the amount of reinforcement in the slab, the type of aggregate (crushed rock and natural gravel), and strength of the concrete. The main conclusions after six years of traffic (4000 commercial vehicles per day) were that only reinforced slabs of 8 in thickness and over, laid on a granular sub-base at least 3 in thick were likely to give a satisfactory long-term performance. Also, it was found that satisfactory pavement-quality concrete could be made using either crushed rock or natural gravel aggregate.

For the flexible pavement, considering only the combinations of the best materials, it was found that parts of the road pavement performed well where the overall thickness of construction was considerably less than the original design thickness based on the equilibrium California bearing ratio of the subgrade. For the rigid pavement, the 8 in thick slabs performed satisfactorily compared to the original design thickness of 10 in. So for both flexible and rigid pavements, it was found that the *Road Note No. 29* recommendations provided a degree of overdesign. This was considered to be a good thing, because it provided a factor of safety sufficient to allow for the variability in quality of construction that occurs in practice on highway construction sites. The importance of the Alconbury Hill experiment was that it gave highway engineers confidence in the *Road Note No. 29* methods of pavement design that were to be used extensively in Great Britain during the decades that followed.

Mechanisation of Road Pavement Construction

In the early years of the twentieth century, there were few mechanical aids to road pavement construction other than the steamroller, the tar boiler and the lorry: most of the activities involved in road construction were carried out by hand. Figure 7.6 shows some of the hand tools in use in 1907. This state of affairs was to be radically altered after the Second World War (1939–45) when the growth of road construction called for increased mechanisation, and much of the equipment for doing this came originally from the United States.

Probably the most important single piece of equipment was the Barber Greene paving machine for laying bituminous surfacing. The machine was 10 ft wide, had a mass of 10 tons, and could lay, tamp and level 80 tons of bituminous material per hour. It could lay surfacing in thicknesses varying from 0.25 in to 6 in, at speeds of up to 11 ft per minute depending upon the thickness being laid. When going well, a considerable fleet of lorries was needed to keep the paver supplied with material. Figure 7.7 shows the basic outlines of one such mechanised bituminous paver that spread, levelled and partly compacted the bituminous mixture. A hopper on the front of the machine received the bituminous material from tipper lorries arriving from the mixing plant. The mix was then fed to augers that distributed it over the required spread width. Then a screed, set to the required thickness, and incorporating a tamper, vibrator and heater, laid the material on the pavement. It was finally compacted by a roller. The paver was self-propelled could be fitted with either pneumatic tyres or caterpillar tracks.

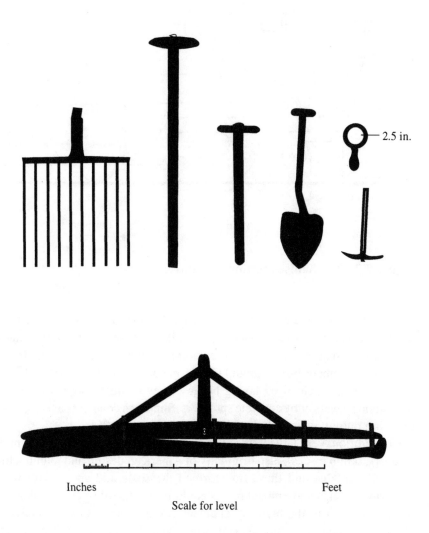

2.5 in.

Inches   Feet

Scale for level

Figure 7.6   Hand tools used for roadmaking, 1907. Top (left–right): fork, hammers, shovel, ring gauge, pick. Bottom: plummet rules (a device for gauging the road surface)

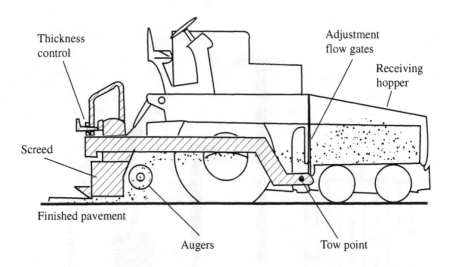

Figure 7.7   Mechanised bituminous paver

Hand-pitched stone roadbases, built in much the same way as in Telford's time, gave place to roadbases of wetmix made with crushed stone or blastfurnace slag, or in areas where natural gravels were available, to lean concrete or cement-bound granular base material. All these materials leant themselves to mechanised laying because they could be spread readily by bituminous pavers or by concrete spreaders. Slip-form concrete pavers, capable of a high output, were introduced to Great Britain in 1965.

In addition, very large items of earthmoving plant (e.g. bulldozers, motor scrapers, dump trucks), also originally of American design and manufacture, became available and these transformed the scale and speed with which highway cuttings and embankments could be built. Although this plant was of great benefit to the highway engineer, unfortunately on some occasions deep cutting and high embankments were made that are, out of scale with the natural landscape.

Pervious Macadam

Anyone who has had the experience of driving on a motorway behind an articulated lorry during very heavy rain will know how appalling is the danger from reduced or lost visibility caused by spray. The problem arises because during very heavy rain the camber of the road surface is not sufficient to drain the water to the sides and water begins to pond on the surface. This ponded water is picked up by vehicle tyres and thrown into the air as spray: the greater the number of wheels the more the spray. One solution to the problem is to drain the water away internally and this is the principle of pervious macadam. Pervious macadam is made from uniformly graded, large-sized aggregate bound together with bitumen, a mix that results in the material containing some 20 per cent of interconnecting air voids, which means that the laid and compacted material is pervious to water. Pervious macadam is laid as the wearing course of the surfacing and is always laid on an impermeable basecourse to prevent water from going right through to the roadbase. Water passing through the pervious macadam is intercepted by the top of the basecourse and drains away to the side of the road to the edge drain as shown in Figure 7.8. Pervious macadam was developed in the 1950s for airfield pavements but, for some reason, was not used on roads until very much later.

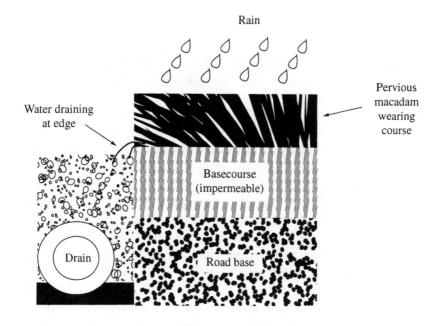

Figure 7.8   The principle of pervious macadam

Following its use in France and the Netherlands, trials were carried out in Great Britain in the early 1990s. The results, at least in the short term, have shown that the material produces a drastic reduction in spray. However, it is not known whether clogging of the pores with dust, oil and rubber from tyres will result in the good effects lasting only for a limited time. The other imponderable factor is whether allowing water into the macadam will accelerate the weathering of the bitumen binder, leading to loss of adhesion of the aggregate particles and resulting in early failure of the wearing course. Also, if water freezes in the pores the pervious macadam, it may be prone to frost loosening in the winter. Another disadvantage of pervious macadam that has already been noticed is that it requires more salt than normal road surfaces in winter to prevent icing. An unexpected advantage of pervious macadam is that it was found to give a quiet running surface, probably because the small cavities in the surface absorb tyre noise. It should be noted that, strictly speaking, pervious macadam should be called pervious bitumen macadam. The places where pervious macadam has been laid on British roads were: A38 Burton Bypass, M40 junctions 6–7, M4 junctions 32–34, and M25 junctions 8–10 clockwise.

* * *

The Second World War was the most important historical event of the twentieth century. The war occurred almost exactly half way through the century and divided it into two periods which can be seen to have profound social, cultural, economic, scientific and technical differences. The economy of the United Kingdom was slow to recover from the war, and for five years or so immediately after it there were rationing, shortages of all kinds of commodities and austerity. In the early 1950s, recovery began and road construction recommenced. However, although conventional roads continued to be built, a completely new type of road – the motorway – began to be constructed in Great Britain, and this is the subject of the next chapter.

To conclude this chapter, Table 7.3 gives a comparison of the two main forms of road construction, bituminous and concrete, for motorways and trunk roads in the United Kingdom as estimated in 1986.

It should be noted that there are some differences between this table and Table 7.1, probably arising from differences in estimating and defining the different categories of pavement and of type of road. Nevertheless, it can be seen that the great majority of British motorways and trunk roads.

Table 7.3   Comparison of bituminous and concrete road construction

Type of road	Bituminous (km)	Concrete (km)	Both (km)
Motorways	1,923	270	2,193
Trunk roads			
Dual carriageway	2,200	250	2,450
Single carriageway	5,400	12	5,412
Total – motorways and trunk roads	9,523	532	10,055

Conservationists sometimes complain that the countryside is becoming 'concreted over' by roads, but Table 7.3 shows that their complaint should more properly be levelled at blacktop rather than concrete. In fact, except in urban areas, roads occupy only a small proportion of the land surface. In 1999 it was estimated that in the United Kingdom there were 13 km of motorway per 1,000 square kilometres. For comparison, the corresponding figure for some other Western European countries were the Netherlands 58 km, Germany 32 km and France 17 km, so that the United Kingdom has a relatively low motorway density.

8 Motorways

Nothing should be allowed to come in the way
of the great car economy

In popular belief, motorways originated in Nazi Germany in the 1930s and were ordered by Adolf Hitler to provide the *Wehrmacht* with the means of deploying motorised forces rapidly across Germany in preparation for the forthcoming European war. Unfortunately, the truth of the matter is much more prosaic and, in fact, we have to go to Italy in the 1920s to find the origin of the motorway. So far in this book all the roads that we have considered have been *all-purpose roads*: that is to say, roads that can carry all kinds of traffic, at any speed, and which are totally interconnected with the general road network. However, the advent of the high speed motor car in the early twentieth century soon gave rise to the idea of the *special road* – one restricted to motor traffic, for high speed, and with only limited access to or from the ordinary road system. The special road was conceived for very fast, long-distance travel by motor car.

Italian and German Motorways

The first motorway (*autostrada*) was planned in 1921 by an Italian engineer, Piero Puricelli. His idea was to connect the city of Milan in northern Italy with the neighbouring towns of Como, Varese and Lake Maggiore with a road tailored specifically to the needs of the motor car. The Italian government approved of the project and in 1922 granted the *Societa Anonima Autostrade* the necessary authorisation to build the motorway. Construction work began in June 1923 and the whole project was completed in September 1925; the total length being 84 km.

The motorway consisted of a single two-way carriageway varying in width from 8.5–10.5 m, separation of opposing traffic being by a continuous dividing line of white paint – looking back it is rather amusing to think that this was considered adequate. As a safety measure, the motorway was fenced off on either side by high metal-wire fencing. The geometry of the road, in both alignment and gradient, was designed for a cruising speed of 60 km/h. A large number of structures was built to carry the motorway over and under the complicated network of existing roads, railways and waterways; this necessitated one structure per 700 m of motorway, together with the construction of about 100 km of new diversions and re-alignments to the existing roads. Structures were designed for a maximum gross vehicle weight of 30 tonnes. Parking was prohibited on the carriageway but for emergency use, unpaved 1.5–2.0 m wide shoulders were provided. After studies of the various kinds of pavement used for motor roads in the United States, the Italian motorway was constructed with a concrete pavement, special continuous mixers and pavers laying the whole width of the carriageway in one pass. The mix proportions were such that each cubic metre of concrete contained 0.75 m^3 crushed stone aggregate, 0.5 m^3 of sand and 350 kg of cement.

The motorway was financed by levying tolls on the traffic, there being four categories: three depending on the horsepower of the engine of the vehicle and the fourth on whether a trailer was being towed. It is unlikely that the motorway was conceived with any military purpose in mind, and its timing in relation to contemporary political events in Italy – namely the coming to power as Prime Minister of Benito Mussolini in 1922 – is no more than a coincidence.

The Milan to Lake Maggiore motorway had all the elements of a modern motorway save one. Firstly, it was reserved exclusively for motor vehicles; secondly, it was designed for high-speed travel; thirdly, it was isolated from the normal road system except at a small number of selected points; and fourthly, its intersections were grade separated. However, there is one other important feature it did not possess – dual carriageways – for as we have seen it had a single carriageway only. On modern motorways it is considered essential to separate the opposing streams of traffic by providing dual carriageways, divided from each other by a central reservation and, latterly, crash barriers as well. The Italians went on to build further single-carriageway motorways until by 1935 they had 485 km of this class of road.

The Italian motorways had a pronounced effect on designs for roads in other countries and one of the first countries to take up the new idea was Germany. In 1934 the German government commenced the building of a network of motorways (*autobahnen*). These roads had dual carriageways, each 7.5 m wide separated by a 3.5–5.0 m wide central reservation, and had no level crossings with other roads. The motorways were designed for speeds of up to 100 km/h. The provision of dual carriageways showed an important advance over the Italian motorways and set the standard for the future. By

September 1939 when the Second World War broke out, 3,200 km of motorway had been built and a further 2,000 km were still under construction.

When the German motorways were examined after the war in 1946, the British inspecting team considered that there was clear evidence that the motorways had not been built for military purposes, although, of course, they had been used in wartime for military traffic. It is much more likely that construction of the motorway network was promoted by the Nazi government because of the external prestige such a scheme conferred upon the state, together with the internal benefit of reducing unemployment. Indeed, on the point of their military usefulness, Albert Speer has related in his book *Inside the Third Reich* how in July 1941 both he and Dr Fritz Todt, who was in charge of the construction industry in Germany, wanted to suspend motorway construction in favour of other projects more essential to the war effort, but were unable to do so because it was one of Hitler's favourite projects. As was the case with the Italian motorways and Mussolini, Hitler's appointment as Chancellor in 1933 seems to be no more than coincidental with the commencement of the German motorways, which were planned in 1933.

Early Plans for Motorways in Great Britain

The Italian and German motorways impressed other road engineers, and in Great Britain in 1936 the Institution of Highway Engineers proposed an ambitious motorway network comprising 51 roads with a total length of 2,800 miles. This was turned down by the Minister of Transport on the grounds that it would be better to improve the existing road system rather than build an entirely new one.

In 1937 the German government organised a visit to the German motorways by a party from Great Britain which included a large delegation of County Surveyors and members of County Councils. Although, inevitably, the Germans exploited the visit for propaganda purposes – 'English roadmakers become acquainted with Adolf Hitler's roads' ran one German newspaper headline – it did provide an opportunity for British local-authority engineers to see motorways at first hand. A fact noted by more than one observer on the visit was the small amount of traffic being carried by the German motorways, and it maybe a sinister interpretation of this which gave rise to the belief that the motorways were being built primarily for military use.

As a result of the visit, the County Surveyors' Society prepared a plan for a national motorway system which was less ambitious, but probably more realistic, than that of the Institution of Highway Engineers. The County Surveyors' Society plan, published in 1938, called for 1,000 miles of motorway linking the main industrial centres of the country as shown in Figure 8.1. The Ministry of Transport again did not look favourably on motorways, saying that the small proportion of through traffic they would attract would not justify the expense of constructing them as against spending the money on improving existing roads. However, by 1939 attitudes had begun to change and a Select Committee of the House of Lords recommended that an experimental motorway, perhaps from London to Birmingham, should be built and the effects on road safety and transportation studied before a full programme of motorway building be put in hand. The outbreak of war in September 1939 put this proposal into abeyance for the duration of hostilities and for some time after. Before leaving these pre-war plans, it is worth noting that the Institution of Highways Engineers scheme included a road that the County Surveyors' Society scheme did not, namely an orbital motorway around London to link up the motorways converging on the capital. This was a far-sighted provision, which as we shall see, was eventually found to be a compelling necessity in the motorway system when it was finally constructed.

During the war years little new road construction took place, there being other more pressing demands on the civil engineering industry, notably the construction of the many new airfields that were necessary in order to defend the country and to prosecute the air-war against Germany. In addition, the existing roads suffered from the additional burden of heavy military traffic, particularly in southern England during the preparation for the Normandy invasion in 1944. After the war there was a backlog of road maintenance and repair to be got through before any programme of motorway construction could be contemplated, even if it could have been afforded in the post-war years of austerity. It was, therefore, not until 1956 that the construction of the first motorway in Great Britain commenced.

Preston Bypass Motorway

In the event, the first motorway was not the London to Birmingham motorway that had been mooted in 1939, but the eight mile long Preston Bypass motorway, later to become part of the M6. It was completed and opened to traffic in December 1958 with much ceremony, only to suffer the ignominy of having to be closed almost immediately afterwards in January 1959 because of extensive breaking-up of the pavement due to frost damage in the roadbase

Figure 8.1   The 1938 proposals for a motorway system

and sub-base of the road. The air temperature during the severe cold spell was as low as 8°F and this was followed by a sudden thaw when the air temperature rose to 43°F.

The pavement of the Preston Bypass motorway consisted of a surfacing made up from a 0.75 in thick fine-cold asphalt wearing course on a 2.5 in tarmacadam basecourse, a roadbase consisting of 9 in of wetmix limestone macadam, and a sub-base of burnt colliery shale which varied in thickness depending upon the underlying soil conditions. In all then, the thickness of surfacing plus roadbase was only 12.25 in given that the full specified thickness had been laid, but there was evidence that in some places it had not, the thickness being in places as little as 10 in; this point will be returned to later. It should be noted that the surfacing was intended to be temporary only, and was in fact put down with a view to a permanent surfacing being laid after any settlement of the road had been allowed to take place. In the summer of 1959 it was replaced by 4 in of hot-rolled asphalt laid in two layers. If this stronger, thicker surfacing had been provided in the first instance, the frost damage may not have been so extensive.

As shown in Figure 1.5 in chapter 1, the mean yearly frost index for the weather station at Preston, only a few miles from the Preston Bypass motorway, is 43 degree days. Using the formula and assumptions stated in chapter 1, this gives a frost penetration of 328 mm, or 13 in, just 0.75 in deeper than the total thickness of surfacing plus roadbase on the motorway. In places where the surfacing was thinner, the frost penetration could have been up to 3 in into the sub-base. This means that the cause of the frost damage could have been due to frost-heave in the burnt colliery shale sub-base since frost penetration could have reached this layer. Contemporary reports also indicate that the wetmix limestone macadam roadbase was wetter than intended when laid because of almost continuous heavy rain during construction. Therefore, even if the damage was not due to frost heave as discussed above, it is likely that frost loosening due to freezing of water in the voids between the limestone particles in the roadbase would have occurred because, as we have seen, the whole of the roadbase was probably frozen. Thus the construction of Britain's first motorway brought home to the road engineer the important fact that in our climate frost is a most potent enemy.

The drainage system for the motorway consisted of longitudinal French drains laid in the central reserve and behind each hard shoulder. As well as dealing with the surface water runoff from the carriageways and other paved areas, the hard shoulders, the verges and the slopes of cuttings, the drains were also intended to control the level of the water table below the formation level of the road. Later, it became clear that this drainage system was quite inadequate to cope with all these sources of water and it was replaced. Therefore, it is very likely that the original drainage system was not able to control the water table in the intended manner; thus the water table may have been within the sub-base instead of below it, thereby contributing to the frost heave discussed above.

The Preston Bypass motorway was built with dual, two-lane carriageways, each 24 ft wide with 8 ft wide hard shoulders, but the central reservation was made of sufficient width to allow widening of each carriageway to three lanes, as was in fact done in 1966. The first section of motorway opened in Great Britain therefore set a precedent for most of the ones that were to follow: it was soon running to capacity and needed widening.

London to Birmingham Motorway, M1

The London to Birmingham motorway, the M1, 74 miles in length, was the first full length motorway to be built in the United Kingdom. It consisted of three parts as shown in Figure 8.2. From south to north these were: (i) the St Albans Bypass, 17 miles in length; (ii) south of Luton to Dunchurch, 55 miles long; and (iii) the Dunchurch Bypass, 2 miles. The reason why the London to Birmingham motorway was built was to give relief to the heavily over-trafficked trunk roads A5 and A6. As mentioned previously, motorways differ from ordinary roads in that they are restricted in use to certain classes of motor vehicle, and the necessary powers for doing this had been anticipated as long before as 1949 by the passing of the Special Roads Act in that year.

The pavement for the motorway, except for the St Albans Bypass, was in flexible construction. The design finally adopted was of a 4 in thick surfacing consisting of a 1.5 in thick hot-rolled asphalt wearing course on a 2.5 in thick hot-rolled asphalt basecourse, a 14 in thick roadbase of dry lean concrete spread in two layers and compacted with rollers, and a hoggin sub-base of 6 in or more in thickness. (The roadbase was originally referred to as cement-bound granular material, a more accurate description than lean concrete.) The design thickness of the surfacing plus roadbase was, therefore, 18 in compared with the 12.25 in thickness on the Preston Bypass. Moreover, both surfacing and roadbase were of potentially stronger materials. Therefore, it can be seen that an improved pavement had been provided for the London to Birmingham motorway but this cannot have been as a result of the experience of the Preston Bypass, because construction of the M1 motorway had started well before

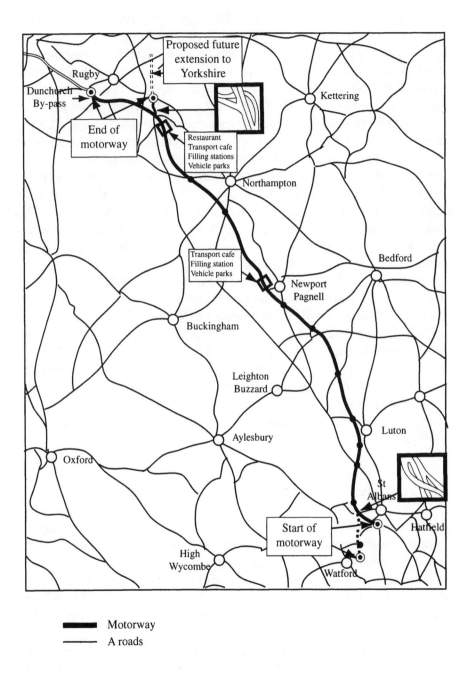

Figure 8.2 London to Birmingham motorway, M1

the failure of the Preston Bypass. The St Albans Bypass was of rigid construction and consisted of an 11 in thick reinforced concrete slab overlying a 7 in thick hoggin sub-base. Therefore, the total thickness of pavement of this section of rigid construction, 18 in, was considerably less than the total thickness of pavement on the flexible construction, 24 in. Construction of the motorway commenced in March 1958 and the road was opened to traffic in November 1959, the 74 miles having taken only 19 months to build. The M1 motorway was officially opened by Ernest Marples, the then Minister of Transport, from an overbridge in Northamptonshire, who professed himself appalled at the speed of the first wave of traffic to pass under him! (in its early years the M1 had no speed limit). Within the first few hours a traffic flow of 1,500 vehicles per hour had been recorded – far more than forecast. The motorway had been designed to have a life of 20 years without major repair, but after three years the first signs of distress were showing, which included surface cracking and poor drainage.

In the early 1980s a reconstruction of the pavement of the M1 motorway was carried out and a thicker, stronger pavement structure was provided to cope with the heavier traffic. It consisted of a 50 mm thick surfacing of rolled asphalt, overlying a roadbase that comprised 275 mm of dense bitumen macadam on 125 mm of rolled asphalt. Beneath this was a 150 mm thick granular sub-base. This in turn rested on a 150 mm thick granular drainage layer with a sheet of geotextile at the interface with the subgrade. The reconstructed pavement therefore had a total thickness of 750 mm compared with 610 mm for the original pavement (an increase of 23 per cent), as shown in Figure 8.3.

London Orbital Motorway, M25

A moment's consideration will show that if a system of radial motorways is built centred on a capital city, then a circular interceptor is an absolute necessity in order to prevent through-traffic from congesting the roads of the metropolis in the course of trying to get from one motorway to another. It will be recalled that this need was recognised as early as 1936 in the Institution of Highway Engineers motorway plan, which included an orbital motorway around London.

In 1937 a Highway Development Survey of Greater London was carried out by C.H. Bressey and Sir Edwin Lutyens, the famous architect, and one of their recommendations was for an orbital road around London. In 1944 the

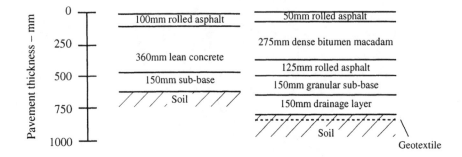

Figure 8.3   Pavement structures for M1 motorway. Left: Original construction. Right: Reconstruction

Greater London Plan by Sir Patrick Abercrombie included no less than four concentric ring roads for London (these were lettered *A* to *D*, going outwards) and an outer orbital road (*E*) lying further out, but whose line was incomplete. In the event, none of these roads was constructed, but the M25 motorway as eventually built, although generally lying further out than the *D* ring, coincides with it for short lengths in the east and north.

The M25 motorway is shown in Figure 8.4. In November 1975 the Ministry of Transport announced that two separate sections of orbital relief road north and south of London would be subsumed into a single motorway ring to be known as the London orbital motorway, M25. Construction started in September 1976, with the section from Westerham to Godstone on the southeast quadrant, and lengths were opened to traffic in a piecemeal fashion as soon as they were usable and had feasible entry and exit points. The final closure of the ring was in October 1986 when the final 21 km section from Micklefield Green to South Mimms on the northwest quadrant was opened to traffic, bringing to completion the 195 km of dual carriageway, three lane motorway.

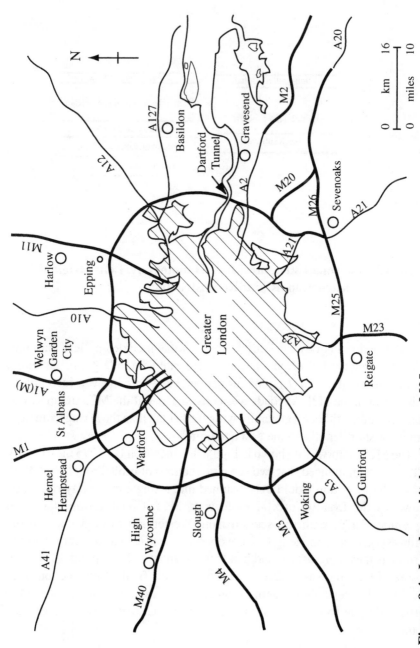

Figure 8.4   London orbital motorway, M25

In accordance with policy current at the time, the Department of Transport decreed that for the M25 they would allow contractors to submit tenders for either flexible (i.e. bituminous) or rigid (i.e. concrete) construction for the road pavement. The outcome was that 54 per cent of the motorway has a flexible pavement and 46 per cent has a rigid pavement – this result is due to the very close tenders which in turn must reflect the very close costs of the two forms of construction. Because the M25 motorway has been built over a long period of time, there were improvement in the pavement design over the construction period. One of these was the introduction of the *capping layer* which is a layer of construction between the sub-base and the soil. The purpose of the capping layer is to provide a construction platform for the road where the subgrade soil is very weak; the material for the capping layer being selected to be stronger than the soil but not of as high quality as the sub-base. A capping layer is only used where the soil has a California bearing ratio of less than 6 per cent. Generalised details of the pavement construction used on the last section of the M25 to be built are shown in Figure 8.5; it shows the two variants of flexible pavement that were used. It can be seen that we now have over 500 mm of construction excluding the capping layer, and up to 1 m if the

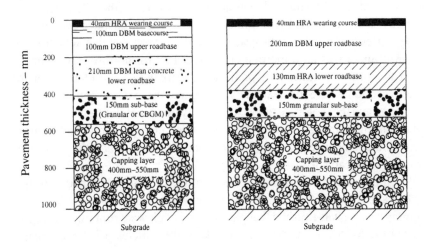

HRA: hot rolled asphalt
DBM: dense bitumen macadam
CBGM: cement-bound granular material

Figure 8.5   Two variants of flexible pavement used on the M25 motorway

capping layer is included. On the Epping section in the northeast quadrant of the M25 the continuously-reinforced concrete road pavement had a slab thickness of 250 mm; the concrete was made of flint gravel with a cement content of 320 kg/m^3, and the reinforcement was placed at mid-depth.

To the east of London the orbital motorway crossed the river Thames by means of the Dartford Tunnel. The first tube, having two lanes carrying two-way traffic, was opened in 1963. Later, a second tube was driven which had a slightly larger cross section but still provided only two lanes; this was opened in 1980, since when each tube has carried one-way traffic. In 1985 the need for yet still higher capacity was recognised and a Dartford Bridge was planned to be constructed alongside the tunnel; this was started in 1988 and completed in 1991. The new bridge, called the Queen Elizabeth II Bridge, carried four lanes of southbound traffic, the four lanes of northbound traffic being carried by the twin tubes of the Dartford tunnel. The whole complex was referred to as the Dartford Crossing.

Before leaving the M25 motorway, two curiosities about it are worth noting; both relate to the claim when it was opened that it was a complete ring of three-lane dual carriageway motorway. Firstly, the motorway was in fact not a complete ring because the short section through the Dartford Tunnel from Dartford to West Thurrock was an all-purpose road (the A282) and not a motorway, so that, subject to the tunnel bye-laws, one might have encountered a wide variety of traffic on this section. (The reason for this was that the Dartford Tunnel was an important cross river link for non-motorway traffic as well as motorway traffic.) Secondly, there were in fact short lengths on the northern section where the nearside lane became the exit and entry lane of an interchange and the motorway consisted of only two-lanes through the junction. This meant that through traffic on the nearside lane was compelled to move over to the centre lane – a very hazardous manoeuvre when the motorway was running to capacity.

When the various completed sections of the M25 were opened to traffic, they had a dramatic effect in reducing journey times, but it was not long after the complete ring was finished that parts of the circuit were running to capacity. By 1994 the M25 was already carrying 165,000 vehicles per day compared with the originally estimated capacity of 100,000 vehicles per day. This may, or may not, be evidence that constructing roads attracts traffic, as is sometimes said. However, the result was that a programme of motorway widening was put in hand which has provided four lanes in place of three over certain congested sections; this work was completed in 1997. It has been estimated that the flow will reach 260,000 vehicles per day by 2000.

Great Britain's Motorway Network

The completion of the M25 motorway in 1986 also marked the completion of most of Great Britain's motorway network. It consists of some 3,000 km of motorway and is shown in Figure 8.6, which also shows the main non-motorway primary routes. For comparison, the total length of the entire road network is 352,000 km, so that motorways account for less than one per cent of all roads.

Stability of Motorway Side Slopes

As has been described, the main phase of motorway construction in Great Britain was between about 1960 and 1980. By 1980 it was apparent that the side slopes on a number of motorways were suffering from instability which manifest itself by shallow slip failures. The method of treating these was to remove the slipped material and replace it with gravel, a process that not only was a wasteful use of a scarce resource (the gravel) but left an unsightly scar on the side slope which remained bare of vegetation. A survey was made in 1980-88 to assess the magnitude of the problem and find the cause. The problem was found to be associated with particular geological formations – mostly the heavy clays – which had been constructed with slope angles that time had shown were too steep. A selection of the results are shown in Table 8.1.

In chapter 1 a description was given of how the highway engineer chooses an angle for the side slope of an embankment or a cutting. It will be recalled that the condition for equilibrium of a slope is:

$$W \sin \theta = S$$

where θ is the angle of the slope to the horizontal, W is the weight of the soil, and S is the shear force resisting movement. It is a straightforward matter to calculate W, and S is determined by carrying out a shear strength test on a sample of soil from the site. The result of the shear strength test will be valid for the slope at the time of construction which explains why the slope is initially stable. However, as time goes by, the effects of rain and weathering cause softening of the near-surface soil in the face of the slope which reduces its shear strength and consequently reduces S, the shear force resisting movement down the slope. If S falls below $W \sin \theta$ the slope will become unstable and may fail.

Figure 8.6   Great Britain's motorway network in 1987

Table 8.1   Geological formations with a high incidence of side slope failures

Clay geological formation	Percentage of failures	Slope angle (degrees)
Embankments		
Gault clay	8.2	22
Reading beds	7.6	27
Kimmeridge clay	6.1	27
Oxford clay	5.7	27
London clay	4.4	27
Cuttings		
Gault clay	9.6	22
Oxford clay	3.2	27
Reading beds	2.9	18

The long-term safe value of θ can be found by examining natural slopes that develop on heavy clays and measuring the steepest one that can be found. This has been done for three of the clay geological formations, and estimated for the other two, and the results are shown in Table 8.2.

Table 8.2   Maximum natural slope angles for some clays

Clay geological formation	Natural maximum slope angle (degrees)
Gault clay	9 measured
Reading beds	10 estimated
Kimmeridge clay	14 measured
Oxford clay	16 estimated
London clay	10 measured

Table 8.2 shows that, for all the clays, the maximum natural slope angles are considerably less than the embankment and cutting slope angles shown in Table 8.1. It can be seen that this has serious implications for the future stability of these slopes, and is a point that will be returned to in chapter 9.

If less-steep slopes were adopted for motorway cuttings and embankments in heavy clays the initial land take would, of course, be much greater than hitherto, and much more earthmoving would be required. However, after construction these low-angle slopes could be topsoiled and returned to agricultural use, and any additional material excavated could be used to blend the motorway earthworks more naturally into the landscape. The low-angle side slopes of some of the cuttings in Gault clay on the M26 motorway in Kent show what can be done.

* * *

It has been a matter of considerable debate whether the building of new roads generates or attracts new traffic. But it has been a matter of common experience that there has been a disproportionately high number of heavy lorries, both British and foreign, on motorways compared with other roads. Figure 8.7 shows the growth in traffic of heavy lorries (i.e. those having five or more axles) on all roads in Great Britain for the period 1981–86. It will be recalled

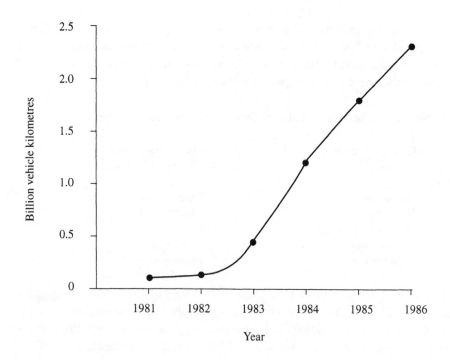

Figure 8.7   Growth in traffic of heavy lorries 1981–86

that motorway construction began at the end of the 1950s, and individual motorways were opened for use as they were built. By about 1980 a basic motorway network was in use, although the final network was not completed until 1986. Referring to Figure 8.6, it can be seen that the growth in traffic in heavy lorries was slow until 1982 but after that it began to climb rapidly. It is suggested that the building of a viable motorway network by 1980 generated or attracted heavy lorry traffic as road hauliers realised the advantages for freight transport that the motorways offered. This trend continued: in 1998 it was estimated that 690,000 foreign lorries per year entered Great Britain, compared with 484,000 per year in 1996 – a growth rate of 21 per cent per year. So the motorway system originally envisaged to be for fast motor car traffic was taken over by heavy lorry traffic.

Road Objectors and Protesters

Throughout almost all of history, roads with the exception of military ones, have been regarded as having a wholly beneficial and civilising influence. Indeed, in medieval times bridge building – if not road building – was regarded as an act of religious piety. Roads improved communication, promoted trade, distributed goods of all kinds, encouraged travel, assisted government and furthered many other desirable ends. And roadmakers were looked upon as benefactors of mankind.

In the 1960s and 1970s when the new motorways were being built, trunk roads being improved and urban road schemes being constructed, these measures too were regarded by the general public with almost universal approbation, apart from the unfortunate individuals whose homes lay directly on line of the road and whose property was compulsorily purchased to make way for it. Motorways, like the railways a century before, were regarded as the very embodiment of modernity and progress. Prestigious new roads were considered to reflect great credit on the government of the day. Indeed, in December 1958 when the first motorway, the Preston Bypass motorway was finished, it was opened with acclamation by the then Prime Minister, Harold Macmillan. In October 1986 when the M25, the last major motorway was completed, although it was opened by no less a personage than the then Prime Minister herself, Mrs Margaret Thatcher, some voices had been raised in criticism of it, so that she was moved to declare: 'Some people are saying that the road is too small. Even that it is a disaster. I must say that I cannot stand those who carp and criticise when they ought to be congratulating Britain on a magnificent achievement.' These remarks neatly encapsulated the then growing polarisation of opinion on new roads: one camp holding that they do not solve the transport problem, the other holding that we should have more of them. And Mrs Thatcher's appeal to British pride in road construction echoes that implied in Vignoles' tabulation (Table 6.3 in chapter 6) of 1870, more than 100 years before.

However, by the 1980s groups of road objectors began to make their opposition to new roads known by making legal objections during the planning enquiries, and when these failed, by protest demonstrations during the construction. The various groups objected to new roads on the following grounds:

direct loss of land as a direct result of the land take;
physical and visual intrusion in the landscape;
artificial barrier separating the community;
air pollution from vehicle exhausts;
noise pollution from vehicle exhausts and tyres;
congestion due to generation of additional traffic; and
sometimes, loss of irreplaceable natural habitat.

While the groups of objectors acted separately, their effectiveness was limited, but when they began to act together they became more difficult to ignore. Road protesters achieved prominence in 1990 by demonstrating against the M3 motorway at Twyford Down near Winchester, and again in 1996 by demonstrating against the Newbury Bypass (A34) where they caused considerable embarrassment and inconvenience to the Department of Transport and the Berkshire County Council respectively. An important feature in both these cases was the presence amongst the protesters of a significant number of respectable middle-class people from the shires who could not be dismissed as cranks. These protests were of no avail in the short term, but the government's long-term response to road objections was tempered by the consideration that these people were voters in future elections. When in November 1998 the 13.7-km long, dual-carriageway Newbury Bypass was opened to traffic, it was done so at 1.25 am and in secrecy in order to forestall the return of the road protesters. This was in marked contrast to the ribbon-cutting ceremonies that had greeted the opening of previous major road schemes. Twyford Down and Newbury have changed the debate on road construction and the balance of opinion in the country seems now to be anti-road. However, it should be borne in mind that many people in Newbury supported the bypass and were delighted with the recovered tranquillity in the town after it was opened. In spite of the success of the road protesters, the Newbury Bypass should not be allowed to be the last bypass to be built in Great Britain.

It must be noted, however, that many road objectors will not be against roads as such, but only against a particular road or alignment. If the road is moved elsewhere some objectors will disappear – only to be replaced by others who object to the new site. So there is an element of 'not in my back yard' in many an objector's motivation. Therefore, it is necessary to take a balanced view of road objections, to be aware that some objectors have an axe to grind, to make a distinction between legitimate complaint and special pleading, and to judge each case on its own merits.

On the matter of road protesters, perhaps we can leave the last word to the Archbishop of Canterbury, Dr George Carey. In 1998, commenting on what he considered to be an imbalance between respect for nature and the needs of local communities, he warned that: 'our anxiety about the countryside leads us to oppose all new buildings or new roads, even when they are not a needless luxury but a necessity to a community'.

9   Conclusion

... and go on till you come
to the end: then stop.

This chapter will make some broad generalisations that emerge from the study of the technical history of roads, and will also make some particular observations that may have some more general validity.

The study has shown that the history of roads in Great Britain covers an immense time span of 2,000 years, far longer than any other system of inland transport (Figure 9.1). And if we include the prehistoric trackways, which date back to 2500 BC, the time span of roads is more than doubled. However, roads have varied in their importance at different times as Figure 9.1 shows.

The total lengths of the road systems constructed at different times throughout history in Great Britain for which we have estimates are shown in Table 9.1. Also shown, for comparison, is the total length of all roads in 1870 and in 1990; the 1870 mileage includes roads in Ireland.

Table 9.1   Lengths of road constructed in Great Britain

Road system	Miles	Kilometres
Main prehistoric trackways	443	713
Roman roads	10,000	16,100
Scottish military roads	1,100	1,771
Turnpike roads	22,000	35,420
Motorways	1,863	3,000
All roads (1870)	160,000	257,488
All roads (1990)	218,815	352,292

The figures in Table 9.1 allows to appreciate the achievements of our predecessors in the field of roadmaking. For example, we are proud of our motorways, but they are less than 20 per cent of the length of the Roman roads.

114

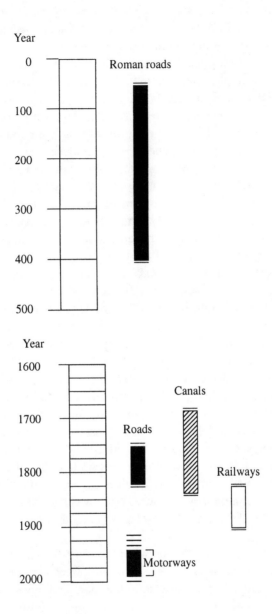

Figure 9.1   Periods of construction and main use of inland transport methods in Great Britain

The history of the Roman roads and the Scottish highland roads has shown that military roads are two-edged swords. Military roads fulfil their purpose in keeping control of the country only so long as a strong army is present. We have seen that during the Napoleonic threat of invasion, steps were taken to destroy roads and thus deny them to the invader. Once the country cannot be adequately defended, the roads become the means whereby an invader can penetrate faster and deeper into the country than would have been the case if there were no roads. The reverse is also true: lack of good roads can protect a weak country. The German general Heinz Guderian has described in his book *Panzer Leader* how during the invasion of Russia in June 1941 there were few paved roads. The earth roads were adequate for carrying the German motorised forces while the roads were dry in the summer, but early in October the onset of wet weather rapidly turned them into 'canals of bottomless mud' along which wheeled vehicles became totally immobilised unless towed by tracked vehicles. On 6 October the first snow fell, but it soon melted turning the landscape into a trackless expanse – the *rasputitsa* – literally the 'time without roads'. If the Russian roads had been paved, the *Wehrmacht* might have succeeded in capturing the whole of Moscow in 1941, instead of just a single tramstop only 12 miles from the centre of the city, with all the implications that the conquest of the capital of the Soviet Union might have had for the outcome of the war.

It will be recalled that the coming of the railways in the mid-nineteenth century led to the decline of coach traffic on the turnpike roads and the eventual demise of the turnpike trusts. By an ironic turn of fate, in the mid-twentieth century, the success of the motor car and the bituminous road led to the decline of the railways, culminating in the widespread closures of lines put in hand by Dr Beeching in the 1960s. It can be seen that the fallacy of this situation lies in the fact that road and rail developed as competing systems of transport rather than as complementary ones. What was needed, both then and now, at the national level is the much talked about but long awaited integrated transport policy.

The railway construction boom of the 1840–90 decades, as well as taking traffic from the roads, had a more insidious effect – they removed talent from road engineering. As the construction of more and more railways took place, there was an enormous demand for civil engineers to survey, design and build the lines, and for mechanical engineers to design and build steam locomotives. Any young engineer with ability and ambition immediately fell under the spell of attraction of the railways, which were the apple of the Victorian public's eye and in which that public was so keen to invest. The railways also poached existing engineers from the roads; for example, Thomas Brassey, probably the most outstanding railway contractor of the nineteenth century, started his career as an assistant surveyor on the Holyhead Road. There can be no doubt that this draining of talent had a contributory effect in allowing the roads to become run down. Here is another might-have-been of the history of technology. If there had been no railways, capable young civil engineers would have found employment in devising and constructing smooth-surfaced roads, and capable young mechanical engineers would have developed and built effective steam-powered road vehicles capable of running on them.

The reader may have noted that a number of early developments in the history of roads took place in France and were then introduced into Great Britain. Among these can be mentioned maybe Tresaguet's stone roads (1775), the use of asphalt in Paris (1854), the steamroller (1859), and the importation of the motor car itself (1895). There is no doubt that the reason for this was the close proximity of England and France together with the practice of observant travellers like Arthur Young who reported what they saw. There is much evidence that in other branches of civil engineering, such as the railways, the flow of ideas was in the reverse direction.

The French are proud of their Revolution and attribute many of the technical improvements in their society and culture to the liberating influence of that momentous event. However, in the case of their fine system of stone roads, it was under the *ancien regime* that they were both initiated and developed. It is an ironic thought that the mobility of Napoleon's armies within France was in large part due to their ability to march swiftly on the pre-Revolutionary Royal roads, such as those shown in Figure 9.2.

From the early decades of the eighteenth century until the end of the twentieth century, road builders have generally tried to 'make the road suit the traffic' in line with McAdam's maxim. However, the traffic for which the road was built has often changed in unexpected ways. Wade and Caulfeild had made the Scottish military roads for marching men and artillery, but in 1750 Caulfeild was rightfully incensed when he discovered the local practice of dragging timber along the roads was destroying them by making large channels in the gravel which led to its erosion by rain water. Later, Perthshire and other counties had to forbid the 'hauling of deals or trees on the roads, as they were made for wheel carriages and were greatly deteriorated by such practices'. In the eighteenth and nineteenth century McAdam and Telford for the turnpike trusts made their roads primarily for fast mail coaches. Although the trusts allowed other traffic to use the roads, in the case of waggons they tried to suit the traffic to the road by stipulating the dimensions of the wagon's

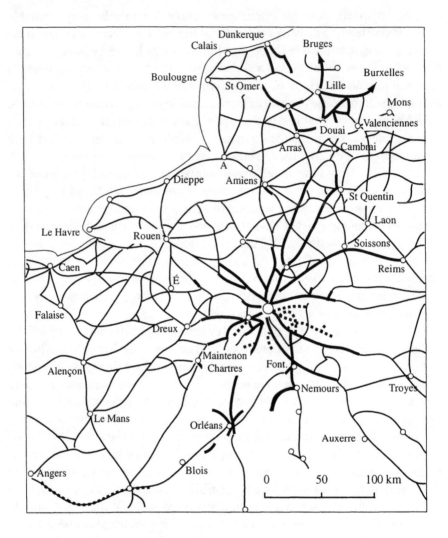

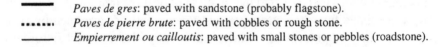

—————— *Paves de gres*: paved with sandstone (probably flagstone).
■■■■■■■ *Paves de pierre brute*: paved with cobbles or rough stone.
—————— *Empierrement ou cailloutis*: paved with small stones or pebbles (roadstone).

Figure 9.2   Small part of the paved French road network in 1789

wheel rims and, in some cases, by charging tolls based on the wagon's weight. In the second half of the twentieth century the first motorways were made for the motor car, but increasing use by heavy lorries led to the need for the pavements to be reconstructed earlier than would have otherwise been the case. Later motorways were designed for heavier traffic but, as discussed below, the time may be approaching when the traffic will have to be suited to the road.

Throughout their history roads have been liable to damage from frost and this has been one of the themes of the book. Frost damage to roads continued to occur well into the second half of the twentieth century, but became less of a problem for later new major roads because of three reasons. Firstly, the increase in traffic loading and intensity resulted in the total thickness of road pavement usually exceeding 450 mm, thereby protecting the subgrade from frost penetration. Secondly, for the same reason of heavy traffic, the road materials used in the surfacing and roadbase were either bituminously bound or of concrete that were not susceptible to frost damage. Thirdly, in the 1950s a laboratory frost heave test was developed to test road materials; this test was further refined in the 1980s. The introduction of the frost heave test meant that sub-base materials were tested before use, ensuring that only ones not susceptible to frost heave were used in the road. The frost heave test also showed that many frost-susceptible materials could be rendered frost-resistant by the addition of a small amount of cement, sometimes only 2 per cent – this was an important finding because it extended the range of potential sub-base materials.

During the nineteenth century period of railway building, tunnels were often used to carry the lines through natural obstructions caused by difficult terrain, and many of the techniques of both hard-rock and soft-ground tunnelling were developed as a consequence. By contrast, when the motorways were built in the second half of the twentieth century, tunnels were rarely used in Great Britain. One reason was that the construction of very deep cuttings was both easy and economical because of the availability of large earthmoving plant and the relatively low cost of fuel to power it. However, in at least two instances, namely in the Chiltern Hills at Stokenchurch on the M40 motorway, and at Twyford Down near Winchester on the M3 motorway, tunnels instead of cuttings would have avoided damaging the scenic, but sensitive, chalk downland landscape. The non-motorway road tunnels at Saltash on the A38, at Lewes (the Cuilfail Tunnel) and at Monmouth (A40), and the M4 motorway tunnel near Newport (the Crindau Tunnel) show what can be done to pass roads through topographical obstructions without damaging the landscape.

In chapter 8 we saw that the basic motorway network is now virtually complete. Any remaining motorways under construction, or proposed, will be restricted to filling gaps in the existing network. And for these, the government has decreed that the motorways shall be designed, built and maintained entirely by private companies: the company is then to be paid 'shadow tolls' by the government, the size of which depends on the amount of traffic using the road over the following 30 years. The National Audit Office has calculated that although the scheme saves the government having to find the capital to pay for the road in the first place, the scheme is much more expensive to the taxpayer when costed over the whole 30 year period than if the government had paid for the road at the time of construction. Of course, this system of financing roads is not new – it is the old turnpike system revived except that the taxpayer not the road user pays the tolls.

One of the first roads to be built under this privately funded arrangement was the A1/M1 link, a 21 km length of three-lane dual carriageway motorway between Leeds and Bramham in West Yorkshire. It was opened in January 1999 but was partly closed five months later for resurfacing. The reason for this was that in order to try and keep future maintenance costs to a minimum, the road-building consortium had used a concrete pavement. The concrete had been given a ribbed surface to provide the surface texture needed for skidding resistance (see Appendix 4) and this had created excessive tyre noise from traffic that could be heard over 3 km away, in spite of the planning inspector's recommendation that a low-noise surface should be used. It is almost beyond belief that this eventuality had not been foreseen because it was the very problem that had led to concrete-surfaced roads being banned in July 1992 (see chapter 7).

Some of the main problem facing the highway engineer in the future will now be touched upon. Roads can be successfully designed and built to carry the anticipated vehicle loads of the future because lorries are unlikely to be allowed to exceed about 40 tonnes because of the limit imposed by the need to avoid overloading and thereby damaging existing road bridges. (The limit for lorries was raised from 32.5 to 38 tonnes in 1983, and will rise to 41 tonnes in 1999.) This means wheel loads for multi-wheel heavy lorries will not increase very much above the 10.5 tonnef per axle maximum that is allowed now, provided that the regulations are complied with. That they were not always complied with in the past is shown by the experience of 1986–87 when one quarter of the 5,732 foreign lorries examined on British roads were found to be so overloaded they had to be prohibited on safety grounds. And spot checks made in 1992 by Kent County Council found that 49 per cent of foreign lorries and 29 per cent of British lorries were overloaded.

It is becoming apparent that roads will not be able to carry the anticipated future traffic volumes. In cities this could lead to the situation known as *gridlock* in which the traffic is so dense and interlocked that it is unable to move at all. Gridlock occurred in a part of east London in the mid-1990s when a lorry became stuck in one of the portals of a Thames road tunnel, and this may well be a portent of things to come. The Department of Transport might be well advised to have available a Chinook helicopter so that when gridlock occurs the offending vehicle, or vehicles, can be plucked out from above in order to free the system. To limit the increasing volume of traffic on motorways, road pricing has been discussed. In the proposals to levy tolls on motorways, one method would be to charge a flat rate for all vehicles, and another would be to charge different rates for cars and commercial vehicles. Or vehicles could be charged according to their wheel loads and number of wheels. It would be relatively simple to instal sensors in the road surface on the approaches to the toll booths that would measure the wheel loads and count the number of wheels on an incoming vehicle; a computer would then do the necessary calculations in time to inform drivers of the correct charge by the time they arrived at the toll booth. Overloaded vehicles would be detected at the same time.

It can be argued that introducing toll booths on the already congested road system would add to the congestion, and that an alternative way of road pricing might be by means of vehicle excise duty. In chapter 7 we saw that, if the fourth power relation is valid, the damaging effect on the road of the passage of a single, fully laden, 36-tonne lorry was the same as that of 18,000 motor cars; it has therefore been suggested that the vehicle excise duty could reflect this difference. In 1998 the annual vehicle excise duty for a 38-tonne lorry was £3,200 whilst that for a private car was £150, a ratio of only 21, showing there is scope for some adjustment in the relative rates of duty levied. It should be noted that this takes no account of distance travelled. However, to be effective, any change to the relative rates of vehicle excise duty for cars and lorries would have to be harmonised throughout the European Union to prevent the 'flagging out' of lorries.

One of the technical problems facing the highway engineer in the future will be motorway reconstruction. Road pavements do not last indefinitely: the surface of the road deflects a tiny amount every time a vehicle passes over it but only part of this deflection recovers, the rest accumulates until ruts begin to form in the wheeltracks and cracks occur in the surfacing. When the ruts reach 25–30 mm depth the road needs to be repaired. Present indications are that heavily trafficked motorways need to be reconstructed after twenty years, with all the disruption to traffic that this involves. Therefore, there is an urgent need to develop road pavement materials that are stiffer (i.e. more resistant to permanent deflection) than at present, and therefore will last longer before they need replacing. One solution would be to combine the best elements of the rigid and flexible pavements in a single composite pavement: namely a concrete roadbase with hot-rolled asphalt surfacing, as shown in Figure 9.3. In the meantime, road cones will be with us for many years.

As the need for road maintenance becomes more pressing there will be problems of how to carry it out without causing congestion to traffic, especially as traffic itself will continue to grow. A foretaste of things to come occurred one day in 1998 when contractors carrying out resurfacing on a section of the westbound carriageway of the M4 north of Chippenham in Wiltshire closed two lanes and the hard shoulder. Within minutes traffic began to back up on the busy motorway and soon the entire westbound carriageway over a distance of 25 miles had come to a standstill. Traffic was delayed for two and a half hours and it was estimated that more than 26,000 vehicles were subjected to the hold up.

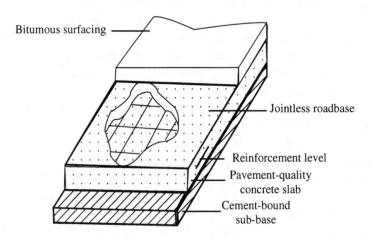

Figure 9.3   Composite pavement structure

Another problem that will become increasingly pressing as time goes by is the instability of motorway side slopes in heavy clay, because it was shown in chapter 8 that the side slope angles of these earthworks are much steeper than the natural maximum slope angles. Fortunately, there are a number of geotechnical solutions available to increase the stability of these embankment and cutting slopes: installation of lime piles or lime-stabilised soil columns, partial reconstruction using geotextiles, and soil nailing.

Finally, looking further into the future, it must be recognised that there is a limit to what the road engineer can do. Traffic cannot go on increasing and expect to find roads increasing indefinitely – there must be other solutions. One thing that could be done is to encourage freight and bulk materials to move off the roads and on to the railways. The firm of Foster Yeoman has shown what can be done, with their railborne aggregate distribution from an inland quarry; the same firm has also pioneered the shipborne distribution of aggregate from a coastal quarry. Both these measures have spared the roads much traffic. Nevertheless, by 1999 it was estimated that in Great Britain 80 per cent of all freight was being carried by road haulage, amounting to some 1.65 billion tonnes of goods per year. So there is still much room for improvement: for example, if just 10 per cent of the goods imported by road in 1998 had been brought in by rail, there would have been 69,000 fewer foreign lorries travelling on British motorways.

Motor vehicle traffic in 1997 was more than eight times that in 1950, and motor car traffic in particular was more than fourteen times greater. The growth in road traffic from 1970 to 1996 is shown in Figure 9.4. For many decades roads in Great Britain were planned on a policy of 'predict and provide' – predict the growth in traffic and then provide the extra roads. However, in 1995 the Standing Advisory Committee on Trunk Road Traffic concluded that new roads generate new traffic and, for the M25 at least, that seems to be most spectacularly true. In 1998 the Highways Agency of the Department of Transport was instructed by the Transport Secretary to concentrate less on road building and more on reducing congestion on existing roads. Thus, as we pass into the third millennium, it seems to be accepted that we may be approaching an end to new road construction and a final limit to the size of the road network in Great Britain; and Figure 9.5, which shows British motorways and major trunk roads in 1998, may represent the high-water-mark of highway development in the country.

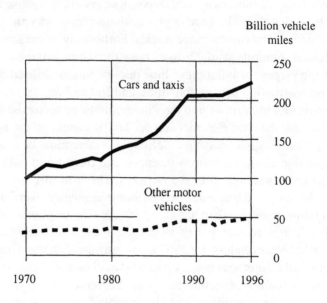

Figure 9.4   Growth in road traffic 1970–96

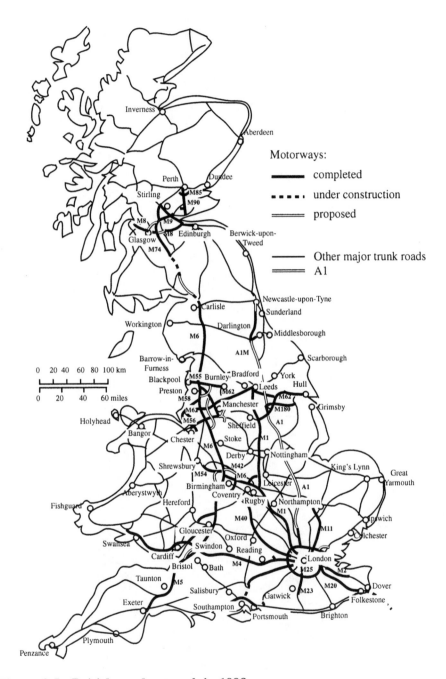

Figure 9.5 British road network in 1998

APPENDICES

Appendix 1
Rocks Used in Road Construction

Geologists divide rocks into three main groups, igneous, sedimentary and metamorphic, according to their mode of formation. *Igneous rocks* are those that have formed from the crystallisation on cooling of molten material, either in the Earth's crust or at the surface. Igneous rocks of deep-seated origin are called *plutonic rocks*, those that have solidified at intermediate depth are called *hypabyssal rocks*, while those that have flowed out or erupted at the surface are called *volcanic rocks*. Igneous rocks are usually strong and hard. *Sedimentary rocks* are formed from fragments, grains and minerals derived from pre-existing rocks by the action of erosion, transport and deposition. They are often layered in appearance due to bedding, caused by variations in composition of the arriving sediment. Indurated sedimentary rocks are usually strong and hard, but non-indurated ones can be weak and soft. *Metamorphic rocks* are formed by the action of heat or pressure (or both) on pre-existing rocks. They are sometimes banded due to segregation or re-crystallisation of minerals during metamorphism. Metamorphic rocks are usually strong and hard.

Rocks are also differentiated on the basis of the size of their constituent crystals or grains. *Coarse grained rocks* are ones in which the crystals or grains can be seen easily with the naked eye, *medium grained rocks* have crystals or grains that can be seen with a x10 hand lens, but in *fine grained rocks* the crystals or grains can only be seen with a microscope. Experienced geologists can identify some coarse grained and medium grained rocks from a hand specimen, but other rocks, particularly if fine grained, require examination in thin section under a polarising microscope for identification.

Using the three rock groups and the three grain-size divisions, a table can be produced into which rocks can be placed and thereby classified. This is a much simplified illustration of the way in which geologists classify rocks. Table A1.1 shows the table with only a single rock name in each category by way of example.

129

Table A1.1 Example of simple rock classification

	Igneous	Sedimentary	Metamorphic
Coarse grained	Granite	Conglomerate	Gneiss
Medium grained	Dolerite	Sandstone	Schist
Fine grained	Andesite	Siltstone	Slate

Igneous rocks are also classified by their quartz content. *Acid* igneous rocks have 10 per cent or more of free quartz, *intermediate* igneous rocks have less than 10 per cent of free quartz, while *basic* igneous rocks have no quartz. In the table above, granite is an acid rock, dolerite is a basic rock and andesite is intermediate.

It is important to realise when looking at the chemical analysis of a rock, that the silica (SiO_2) content is not necessarily the same as the quartz content. The reason for this is that many rocks contain silicates which contribute to the SiO_2 content on chemical analysis. For example, a granite may have a silica content of 71 per cent, but a quartz content of only 22 per cent.

It should be noted that rock types are not unique entities like species of plants and animals, but can vary in composition and properties, and intermediate or mixed types can occur.

Rocks are also categorised by their geological age (starting from the oldest: Precambrian, Cambrian, Ordovician, Silurian, Devonian, Carboniferous, Permian, Triassic, Jurassic, Cretaceous, Tertiary, Quaternary) but this is not of great relevance to their use as roadstones, except for United Kingdom sedimentary rocks which tend to be more indurated with age.

Geologists use the term *Drift* to describe collectively all the superficial materials that are found on the land surface such as glacial, terrace and alluvial deposits; while the term *Solid* is used to describe collectively all the geological formations older than and beneath the Drift. Geological maps of an area are often published in two versions – a Drift edition, showing all the superficial materials; and a Solid edition, showing the geology that would be seen if all the superficial materials were removed.

Table A1.2 shows the main types of rock that are used in road construction, principally as aggregates in bituminous and concrete pavements. The description are simplified. The following abbreviations are used in the table: igneous (I), metamorphic (M), sedimentary (S).

Table A1.2   Main rocks used in road construction

Rock type	Description
Andesite (I)	Fine-grained, usually volcanic, variety of diorite
Arkose (S)	Type of sandstone or gritstone containing over 25% feldspar
Basalt (I)	Fine-grained, basic rock, similar in composition to gabbro, usually volcanic
Breccia (S)	Rock consisting of angular unworn rock fragments bonded by a natural cement
Chalk (S)	Fine-grained, soft, white limestone
Chert (S)	Cryptocrystalline silica
Conglomerate (S)	Rock consisting of rounded pebbles bonded by a natural cement
Diorite (I)	Intermediate plutonic rock, consisting mainly of plagioclase, with hornblende, augite or biotite
Dolerite (I)	Basic rock, with grain size between that of gabbro and basalt
Dolomite (S)	Rock or mineral composed of calcium magnesium carbonate
Flint (S)	Cryptocrystalline silica originating as nodules or layers in the chalk
Gabbro (I)	Coarse-grained, basic, plutonic rock, consisting essentially of plagioclase and pyroxene, sometimes with olivine
Gneiss (M)	Coarsely banded metamorphic rock
Granite (I)	Coarse-grained, acid, plutonic rock consisting essentially of feldspars and quartz, sometimes with mica
Granulite (M)	Metamorphic rock with granular texture
Greywacke (S)	Impure sandstone or gritstone, composed of poorly sorted fragments of quartz, other minerals and rock; the coarse grains usually cemented in a fine matrix
Gritstone (S)	Sandstone with coarse angular grains
Hornfels (M)	Thermally metamorphosed rock containing silicate minerals
Limestone (S)	Sedimentary rock consisting predominantly of calcium carbonate
Marble (M)	Metamorphosed limestone
Microdiorite (I)	Intermediate rock with grain size between diorite and andesite

Table A1.2 cont'd

Microgranite (I)	Acid rock with grain size between granite and rhyolite
Quartzite (M & S)	Metamorphic or sedimentary rock composed almost entirely of quartz grains
Rhyolite (I)	Fine-grained or glassy, acid rock, usually volcanic
Sandstone (S)	Sedimentary rock composed of sand grains bonded by a natural cement
Schist (M)	Finely banded metamorphic rock, often contains mica
Siltstone (S)	Sedimentary rock composed of indurated silt particles
Slate (M)	Fine-grained metamorphic rock with cleavage planes
Syenite (I)	Intermediate plutonic rock, consisting mainly of feldspars with hornblende, biotite or augite
Trachyte (I)	Fine-grained, usually volcanic, type of syenite
Tuff (I)	Indurated volcanic ash

Appendix 2
Soils Used in Road Construction

In civil engineering, *soils* are defined as any loose, or non-indurated, or soft, naturally occurring materials found at or near the Earth's surface – in practice this means any materials that can be excavated using a bulldozer. By contrast, *rocks* are hard naturally occurring materials that require ripping or blasting for excavation. Geological Drift deposits (see Appendix 1) are regarded by the engineer as soils. This special use of the word *soils*, which differs from its use by pedologists, geologists and even laymen, has led to the use of the expression *engineering soils* when a clear distinction needs to be made.

Engineering soils can be considered to fall broadly into three groups: residual soils, transported soils and non-indurated geological formations. *Residual soils* are those formed in place by the direct weathering of rocks. In cold and cool-temperate climatic zones they are usually fairly thin because weathering is slow. In hot and warm-temperate regions residual soils may be thick because weathering is rapid.

Transported soils have been carried to their present location by the action of some natural transporting agent such as water, ice or wind. Examples are the alluvial and estuarine deposits in river valleys and estuaries, and the tills and morainic deposits produced by glacial action. *Non-indurated geological formations* are often referred to as soils by the engineer. Examples are the Oxford Clay, the Keuper Marl, and some of the Cretaceous and Tertiary clay and sand formations.

Engineering soils are classified using their properties of *particle size* (or *grading*) and their *cohesion* (i.e. their ability to stick together). The basic soil types are shown in Table A2.1.

However, soils often occur as mixtures of the basic types, so that the terms for the basic types can be combined to give names for composite soil types, as shown in Table A2.2.

The basic soil types can be referred to using the simple symbols: gravel (G), sand (S), silt (M), clay (C), organic soils (O), and peat (Pt). The symbols may then be combined to give symbols for composite soils, as shown in Table

Table A2.1 Basic soil types

Basic soil types	Particle size (mm)
Granular soils	
Gravel	2–60
Sand	0.06–2
Cohesive soils	
Silt	0.002–0.06
Clay	less than 0.002
Cohesive soils – organic	
Organic clay or silt	Varies
Peat	Varies

A2.2. The symbols (W) and (P) denote soils that are well graded (have a good range of particle sizes) and poorly graded (have a restricted range of particle sizes) respectively.

A particular example of a composite soil type is hoggin. *Hoggin* is a naturally occurring mixture of well-graded flint gravel and sand that contains just enough silt and clay to give the whole mass cohesion without becoming soft in wet weather. Before the days of surfaced roads, hoggin was much prized as a roadmaking material in the south of England. And it is still used for lightly trafficked estate roads and driveways.

Soils, and their properties, are of primary importance to the road engineer because they constitute the subgrade of the road and are used in the construction of earthworks such as cuttings and embankments. In fact, soil used for highway earthworks is by far the greatest road construction material in terms of the quantity employed. But soils are also of interest because gravels and sands find use as sub-base materials and as aggregates for bituminous and concrete pavement construction.

Table A2.2 Composite soil types

Soil types and names					BSCS symbols
	Gravel and *sand* may be designated sandy *gravel* and gravelly *sand*				(GS) (SG)
Granular soils	*Coarse soils* less than 35% of the material is finer than 0.06 mm	*Gravels* More than 50% of coarse material is of gravel size (coarser than 2 mm)		Well graded *gravel* Poorly graded *gravel*	(GW) (GP)
				Silty *gravel* Clayey *gravel*	(G–M) (G–C)
				Very silty *gravel* Very clayey *gravel*	(GM) (GC)
		Sands More than 50% of coarse material is of sand size (finer than 2 mm)		Well graded *sand* Poorly graded *sand*	(SW) (SP)
				Silty *sand* Clayey *sand*	(S–M) (S–C)
				Very silty *sand* Very clayey *sand*	(SM) (SC)
Cohesive soils	*Fine soils* more than 35% of the material is finer than 0.06 mm	Gravelly or sandy *silts* and *clays* 35% to 65% fines		Gravelly *silt* Gravelly *clay*	(MG) (CG)
				Sandy *silt* Sandy *clay*	(MS) (CS)
		Silts and *clays* 65% to 100% fines		*Silt* *Clay* Silty *clay*	(M) (C) –
	Organic soils			Example: organic *silt*	(MO)
	Peat			Fibrous or amorphous *peat*	(Pt)

Source: adapted from BS 5930, 1981.

Appendix 3
Modern Road Materials

Bituminous Pavements

The basic structure of a bituminous pavement is shown in Figure 1.1 of chapter 1. The main structural function of the bituminous pavement is to spread the load applied by the traffic over a sufficiently wide area of the subgrade such that the bearing capacity of the soil is not exceeded.

The principle elements of the bituminous pavement are the surfacing and the roadbase, and the materials from which these are made are basically of two kinds: rolled asphalt and coated macadam.

Rolled asphalt, or *hot-rolled asphalt*, is a high quality bituminous surfacing material that is used for heavily trafficked roads. There are separate specifications for wearing course and base course mixtures. Rolled asphalt consists of a matrix of sand, fine mineral-powder filler and bitumen into which coarse aggregate is added 'like raisins in a pudding'. The coarse aggregate content can vary between none and 65 per cent of the total aggregate. Mixes with a lower stone content (less than 55 per cent) have a smooth surface texture and are used for wearing courses, and mixes with a higher stone content (55–65 per cent) are used for base courses of surfacings. Also, the higher stone content asphalts are sometimes used for roadbases. To improve the skidding resistance of the wearing course, *coated chippings* (of 20 mm or 14 mm nominal size) are spread and rolled into the surface while the asphalt is still workable. Traditionally, specifications for rolled asphalt were in the form of 'recipes' giving the compositions to be used for different traffic and climatic conditions, but latterly, mechanical testing regimes are used to design mixes. With asphalts, the strength of the material is derived mainly from the cohesion provided by the matrix of sand, filler and binder.

Coated macadam (or *bitumen macadam*) consists of crushed rock or natural gravel aggregate coated with bitumen. Coated macadams are mainly 'open textured', that is to say they are mixes containing stone of predominantly one size with a small proportion of finer aggregate (less than 20 per cent) to provide some stability. Coated macadam is used mainly for roadbase. But for less heavily trafficked roads it can also be used for the base course and wearing course of the surfacing. One special type of coated macadam that is coming into use for surfacing is the *pervious macadam* discussed in chapter 7. Coated macadams come in an immense range of mixes designed for different applications – there are even 'medium textured' and 'close textured' macadams that are dense mixes approaching the composition of asphalt for use on heavily trafficked roads. With coated macadams, the strength of the material is derived mainly from the interlocking of the coarse aggregate particles.

The *roadbase* of a bituminous road can be made from a variety of materials. For heavily trafficked roads the roadbase will usually be of coated macadam or lean concrete, but for less heavily trafficked roads it can be of wetmix, crushed hardcore or cement-bound gravel. The *sub-base*, the lowest structural level of the pavement, is usually gravel or sand, sometimes stabilised with cement, or it can be some essentially granular industrial waste material like pulverised fuel ash or quarry scalpings.

Concrete Pavements

The basic structure of a concrete pavement is shown in Figure 1.2 of chapter 1. As with the bituminous pavement, the main structural function of the concrete pavement is to spread the load applied by the traffic over a sufficiently wide area of the subgrade such that the bearing capacity of the soil is not exceeded.

The principal element of a concrete road, the concrete *slab*, is not generally cast directly on the subgrade, but on a thin layer of granular material (e.g. gravel, sand) called the *sub-base* which is placed on the soil first. (In the road industry, concrete pavements are sometimes called *rigid pavements*, in contrast to bituminous pavements which are called *flexible pavements* – this terminology reflects their different material properties.) The load-carrying capacity of the concrete road structure depends mainly on the structural rigidity of the slab and so long as a concrete slab remains in sound condition it will perform its structural function satisfactorily. One section of concrete slab is separated from another by regularly spaced, vertical *joints*, and the traffic load is transferred across the joints by horizontal steel connectors called *dowel-bars*.

Concrete is strong in compression but weak in tension. Because of this plain concrete slabs tend to be prone to cracking, and to prevent from happening the concrete slab is often reinforced with steel. Traditionally, therefore, there have been two basic methods of constructing concrete road pavements, and these are the *jointed unreinforced concrete road pavement* and the *jointed reinforced concrete road pavement*: they are shown in Figure A3.1, and make up the majority of concrete roads in the United Kingdom. Joints tend to be troublesome, so that in addition to these two methods there is another type of construction that came into use in the 1980s, the *unjointed continuously reinforced concrete road pavement*, which is also shown in Figure A3.1; as its name indicates, this slab has no joints. It should be added that roads made from bituminous surfacing materials sometimes have a lean concrete roadbase.

The cement used for making pavement-quality concrete is normally ordinary Portland cement, but sometimes Portland blastfurnace cement is used in areas where it is readily available. Rapid-hardening Portland cement is used for urgent repairs to concrete slabs. Sometimes pulverised fuel ash is used to replace 25–35 per cent of the cement in pavement-quality concrete in order to improve workability and durability, and to provide some protection against alkali-aggregate reaction. Both crushed rock and natural gravel and sand aggregates are suitable for making pavement-quality concrete. All types of concrete road pavements can be laid using either fixed-form or slipform pavers. Traditionally, roads made of unreinforced or reinforced concrete are designed to have a life of 40 years, but many have exceeded this.

For both flexible and rigid pavements, since the late 1980s, if the bearing capacity of the subgrade soil is very low (California bearing ratio of 5 per cent or less) a capping layer is spread on the subgrade before the sub-base is laid. The *capping layer* is a material of lower quality than the sub-base but of higher quality than the subgrade. As well as assisting in load-spreading, the capping layer provides a working platform for construction of the road. Capping layer material can be any locally available gravelly or sandy soil, or some essentially granular industrial by-product or waste material such as burnt colliery shale.

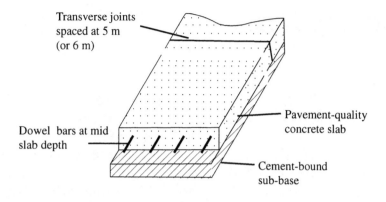

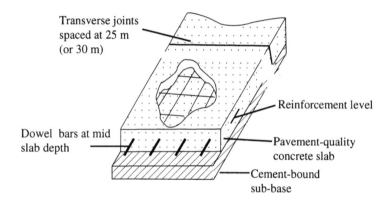

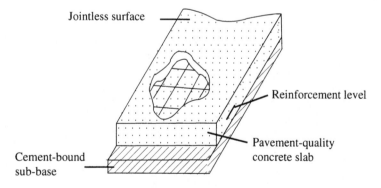

Figure A3.1 Jointed unreinforced (top) and jointed reinforced (centre) concrete road pavements. Unjointed continuously reinforced concrete road pavement (bottom)

Appendix 4
Skidding Resistance

Vehicles can skid on both wet and dry roads. However, skidding is more likely, and more severe, on wet roads. For this reason, skidding resistance is predominantly a matter of concern in the wet. Figure A4.1 represents the forces acting on a motor car braking on a road. They are N a normal force acting vertically downwards, and F a horizontal force acting to bring the car to rest. At the moment when skidding occurs

$$F = \mu N$$

where m is the coefficient of friction between the rubber of the car tyres and the material of the road surface. The normal force N is given by

$$N = Mg$$

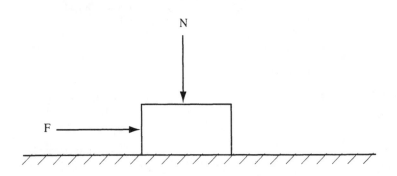

Figure A4.1 Forces acting on a braking car

where M is the mass of the car and g is the acceleration due to gravity. The highway engineer can do nothing about the magnitude of N because M depends on the particular car being considered, and g is a constant. However, the highway engineer wants F to be as large as possible, so he or she endeavours to make μ as large as possible.

It has been found that the coefficient of friction of the road surface depends predominantly on the coefficient of friction of the aggregate that is in the running surface of the road. For bituminous roads, this is the aggregate in the wearing course, or the aggregate used for coated chippings. To provide high skidding resistance, the engineer, therefore, needs to select an aggregate with a high coefficient of friction. Aggregates are tested for skidding resistance after having subjected them to a laboratory regime of accelerated polishing using an apparatus with a loaded rubber tyre, to simulate trafficking on the road. The coefficient of friction between aggregate and rubber is then measured wet using a pendulum device carrying a rubber slider, and the result, multiplied by 100, is called the *polished stone value*. The higher the polished stone value, the greater will be the skidding resistance of the road surface. Table A4.1 gives some idea of mean values for different groups of roadstone.

Table A4.1 Some polished stone values

Group of roadstone	Polished stone value
Crushed rock aggregates	
Dolerites	57
Granites	56
Sandstones	66
Limestones	56
Natural gravel aggregates	
Flint gravels	41
Quartzite gravels	50

The frictional properties of a stone derives from the fine texture, called the *microtexture*, of its surface. Because of this it is easy to see how gritstones (sandstones composed of coarse angular grains) are highly prized as skid-resistant roadstones for surfacing. Aggregates with a high polished stone value are at a premium. Therefore, the highway engineer selects a suitable aggregate for the expected intensity of traffic on the road, and the severity of the site, approaches to junctions, for example, calling for a higher polished stone value than the open road. In situations where very high values are required (70–75), such as approaches to traffic lights on busy roads, an artificial aggregate, calcined bauxite, is used.

The skidding resistance of concrete roads is somewhat different. On a new concrete slab, the surface consists of *laitance*, a material formed by segregation of mortar from the mix during finishing of the surface. The hardened laitance has the texture of sandpaper and provides good skidding resistance while the road is relatively new. However, over the course of time, the laitance is worn away by trafficking and the aggregate becomes exposed at the surface. For this reason, a aggregate with a high polished stone value is used in the mix for the slab, at least for the surface layer, of a concrete road.

For both bituminous and concrete roads, in addition to skidding resistance, a good surface texture is required in order to drain away water from the interface between the tyre and the road in wet weather. This is called the *macrotexture* to distinguish it from microtexture (see Figure A4.2). On bituminous roads the macrotexture is provided by the individual chippings standing a little proud of the overall road surface. On concrete roads the macrotexture is provided by lightly brushing the surface before it hardens which produces a pattern of ridges and grooves. For reasons that are not fully understood, macrotexture also provides safety benefits on dry roads.

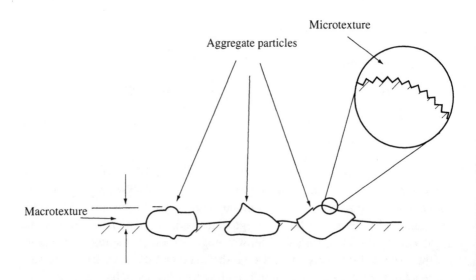

Figure A4.2 Microtexture and macrotexture

From about the 1950s, quite independently of the approach described above, the subject of skidding resistance was also engaging the attention of the tyre manufacturer and the automobile engineer, and this led to two important developments. The first was the production of car tyres made from energy-absorbing high-hysteresis rubber; the second was the introduction of anti-lock braking systems for cars. Both these measures have also contributed to the reduction of skidding accidents. However, to be effective, both high-hysteresis rubber tyres and anti-lock braking systems depend on a basically frictional road surface.

The United Kingdom probably has the most sophisticated policy in the world for providing skidding resistance on roads, and there can be little doubt that this policy is one of the reasons for the country having one of the lowest annual road death rates in Western Europe (see Table A4.2).

Table A4.2   Road deaths in Western Europe in 1992

Country	Road deaths per 100 000 population
Portugal	34
Greece	20
Spain	20
Luxembourg	19
Belgium	17
France	17
Italy	14
Germany	13
Eire	12
Denmark	11
Netherlands	8
United Kingdom	7.6

Select Bibliography

Some of the following texts are relevant to more than one chapter but the citations are not repeated.

Chapter 1

Anderton, P. and Bigg, P.H. (1969), *Changing to the Metric System*, HM Stationery Office, London.

British Standards Institution (1967), 'Glossary of Highway Engineering Terms', *British Standard* BS 892:1967, British Standards Institution, London.

Jacobs, J.C. and West, G. (1966), 'Investigations into the Effect of Freezing on a Typical Road Structure', *Report* 54, Road Research Laboratory, Crowthorne.

Sherwood, P.T. and Roe, P.G. (1986), 'Winter Air Temperatures in Relation to Frost Damage in Roads', *Research Report* RR45, Transport and Road Research Laboratory, Crowthorne.

Chapter 2

Addison, Sir William (1980), *The Old Roads of England*, B.T. Batsford Ltd, London.

Jennet, S. (1976), *The Ridgeway Path*. HM Stationery Office, London.

McKie, R. (1989), 'Bog Roads Reveals Sophisticated Ways of 4000 BC, *Observer*, 12 November.

Raftery, B. (1990), *Trackways Through Time*, Headline Publishing, Rush (Co. Dublin).

Rainbird Clark, R. (1970), *Grime's Graves, Norfolk*, HM Stationery Office, London.

Taylor, C. (1994), *Roads and Tracks of Britain*, Orion Books Ltd, London.

Trevelyan, G.M. (1962), *A Shortened History of England*, Penguin Books, Harmondsworth.

Webster, G. and Dudley, D.R. (1973), *The Roman Conquest of Britain*, Pan Books Ltd, London.

Winbolt, S.E. (1945), *Britain BC*, Penguin Books, Harmondsworth.

Chapter 3

Hindle, B.P. (1984), *Roads and Trackways of the Lake District*, Moorland Publishing Co. Ltd, Ashbourne.

Margary, I. (1967), *Roman Roads in Britain*, revised edn, Baker.

Chapter 4

Defoe, D. (1724), *A Tour Thro' the Whole iIsland of Great Britain, Divided into Circuits or Journies*, London.

Hill, D. (1996), *A History of Engineering in Classical and Medieval Times*, Routledge, London.

Kennish, J. (1991), *Turnpike Roads in Berkshire: a resource pack for schools*, Berkshire Humanities Centre, Reading.

Webb, S. and B. (1963), *The Story of the King's Highway*, Frank Cass and Co. Ltd.

Chapter 5

Steel, T. (1984), *Scotland's Story – A New Perspective*, Collins, London.

Taylor, W. (1976), *The Military Roads in Scotland*, David and Charles, Newton Abbot.

Chapter 6

Bird, A. (1973), *Roads and Vehicles*, Arrow Books Ltd, London.

Derry, T.K. and Williams, T.I. (1973), *A Short History of Technology*, Oxford University Press, Oxford.

Law, H. and Clark, D.K. (1907), *The Construction of Roads and Streets*, 7th (revised) edn, Crosby Lockwood and Son, London.

Ransom, P.J.G. (1984), *The Archaeology of the Transport Revolution 1750–1850*, World's Work Limited, Tadworth.

Reader, W.J. (1980), *Macadam: The McAdam family and the turnpike roads 1798–1861*, William Heinemann Ltd, London.

Rolt, L.T.C. (1986), *Thomas Telford*, Penguin Books, Harmondsworth.

Yvon, M. (1985), 'Pierre-Marie-Jerome Tresaguet, Ingenieur des Ponts-et-Chaussees (1716–1796)', *Colloque 'Les Routes du Sud de la France'*, pp. 295–318.

Chapter 7

British Aggregate Construction Materials Industries (1985), *What's in a Road?*, British Aggregate Construction Materials Industries, London.

Croney, D. (1977), *The Design and Performance of Road Pavements*, HM Stationery Office, London.

Croney, D. and Loe, J.A. (1965), 'Full-scale Pavement Design Experiment on A1 at Alconbury Hill, Huntingdonshire' (Paper No 6848), *Proceedings of the Institution of Civil Engineers*, 30, pp. 225–70.

Hawkins, M. (1988), *Devon Roads*, Devon Books, Exeter.

Newland, D. (1990), 'Roads to Ruin', *New Scientist*, 15 December, pp. 37–44.

O'Flaherty, C.A. (1986), *Highways. Volume 1: Traffic planning and engineering*, 3rd edn, Edward Arnold, London.

O'Flaherty, C.A. (1988), *Highways. Volume 2: Highway engineering*, 3rd edn, Edward Arnold, Sevenoaks.

Road Research Laboratory (1960), *Road Note No 29: A guide to the structural design of flexible and rigid pavements for new roads*, HM Stationery Office, London.

Chapter 8

Baker, J.F.A. (1960), 'The London-Birmingham Motorway: The general motorway plan' (Paper No 6442), *Proceedings of the Institution of Civil Engineers*, 15, pp. 317–32.

Charlesworth, G. (1984), *A History of British Motorways*, Thomas Telford Ltd, London.

Department of Transport (1986), *The M25 Orbital Motorway*, Central Office of Information, London.

Department of Transport (1987), *Transport statistics, Great Britain, 1976–1986*, HM Stationery Office, London.

Mangarano, A. and Pellizzi, G. (1970), 'Italy's First Motorways', *AIPCR-PIARC 1909–1969*, Permanent International Association of Road Congresses, Paris, pp. 129–40.

Perry, J. (1989), 'A Survey of Slope Condition on Motorway Earthworks in England and Wales', *Research Report* RR199, Transport and Road Research Laboratory, Crowthorne.

Special issue: 'M25 London Orbital Motorway' (November 1986), *Highways and Transportation*, 33, (11), pp. 6–53.

Yeadon, H. (1990), 'Early Development of the Motorway System in the North West', *Highways and Transportation*, 4, (37), pp. 19–21.

Chapter 9

British Cement Association (1994), *Concrete Pavements for Highways,* Publication 46.030, British Cement Association, Crowthorne.

House of Commons Committee of Public Accounts (1988), *Regulation of Heavy Lorries*, HM Stationery Office, London.

Jacobs, J.C. (1965), 'The Road Research Laboratory Frost Heave Test', *Laboratory Note* LN/766, Road Research Laboratory, Harmondsworth.

Leathley, A. (1999), 'Noise Flaw Shuts New £200m Motorway Link, *The Times*, 28 June, p. 9.

Roe, P.G. and Webster, D.C. (1984), 'Specification for the TRL Frost Heave Test', *Supplementary Report* SR829, Transport and Road Research Laboratory, Crowthorne.

Webster, D.C. and West, G. (1989), 'The Effects of Additives on the Frost Heave of a Sub-base Gravel', *Research Report* RR213, Transport and Road Research Laboratory, Crowthorne.

Appendix 1

British Standards Institution (1989), 'Methods for Sampling and Testing of Mineral Aggregates, Sands and Fillers. Part 102. Methods for Sampling', *British Standard* BS 812: Part 102: 1989, British Standards Institution, London.

Appendix 2

British Standards Institution (1981), 'Code of Practice for Site Investigations', *British Standard* BS 5930: 1981, British Standards Institution, London.

Appendix 3

British Aggregate Construction Materials Industries (1985), *What's in a Road?,* British Aggregate Construction Materials Industries, London.

British Cement Association (1994), *Concrete Pavements for Highways,* Publication 46.030, British Cement Association, Crowthorne.

Appendix 4

British Standards Institution (1989), 'Methods for Sampling and Testing of Mineral
Aggregates, Sands and Fillers. Part 114. Method for Determination of Polished
Stone Value', *British Standard* BS 812: Part 114: 1989, British Standards
Institution, London.

Glossary

Some terms that are adequately defined in the text when first used have not been repeated here.

Asphalt Mixture of finely crushed rock or sand, mineral filler and bituminous binder suitably proportioned to give a very dense and strong roadmaking material.

Agger The raised earth bank on which the surface of a Roman road was laid.

Aggregate Crushed rock or natural gravel used for construction purposes.

Bearing capacity The ability of the ground to accept loading.

Bitumen Black viscous liquid consisting of a mixture of hydrocarbons obtained as a by-product of distilling petroleum.

Bitumen macadam Coated macadam in which the binder is bitumen.

Bituminous Containing tar or bitumen.

Brickearth Sandy silty clay.

California bearing ratio Measure of the bearing capacity of the subgrade.

Camber Convex surface of the road profile intended to shed rainwater to the sides.

Carriageway That part of the road constructed for the use of vehicles.

149

Capping layer	A layer of material placed between the subgrade and the sub-base when the subgrade is very weak.
Causeway	A road raised above water level or the level of the adjoining ground.
Cement	A powder made by heating a mixture of limestone and clay that sets and hardens when mixed with water.
Cement-bound granular material	Natural gravel stabilised with cement. Used for roadbase and sub-base.
Central reserve	Area separating the carriageways of a dual-carriageway road.
Chalk	Fine-grained, soft white limestone occurring extensively in southeast England.
Chippings	Small single-size pieces of aggregate.
Clay	Mineral particles less than 0.002 mm in size. A soil or deposit consisting predominantly of these.
Cobbles	Rounded pieces of stone 60–200 mm in size.
Concrete	A mixture of aggregate, sand, water and cement that sets and hardens to a solid mass.
Cutting	An open, elongated excavation for carrying a road below ground level.
Dense bitumen macadam	Dense, high quality, bitumen macadam used mainly for roadbase on heavily trafficked roads.
Dualling	Converting a single-carriageway road into a dual-carriageway road by building a second carriageway parallel to the original road.

Earthworks	Cuttings and embankments for roads.
Embankment	An elongated mound of soil or rock constructed to carry a road above ground level.
Fines	Silt and clay.
Flagging out	Registering (licensing) lorries in another country in order to take advantage of lower vehicle excise duty.
Flint	A hard brittle rock consisting of silica (SiO_2). Occurs as nodules in the chalk and as a constituent of many gravels.
Formation	(In roadmaking) the finished surface of the subgrade. (In geology) a geological stratum comprising material of the same composition and age, e.g. London Clay.
Footway	That part of a road constructed for the use of pedestrians.
Fourth power relation	Indication that the damaging effect of traffic varies as the fourth power of the wheel load.
French drain	A drain consisting of pipes with open joints laid in a trench backfilled with gravel.
Frost index	Number of days on which the temperature is continuously below zero multiplied by the number of degrees Celsius below zero.
Geotextile	Plastic material in sheet form used to reinforce or protect soil. Perforated geotextiles are used to assist drainage.
Graded	A graded aggregate is one of specified or controlled particle size.
Grade separation	The crossing of two roads at different levels.
Gravel	Rock fragments or particles 2–60 mm in size. A soil or deposit consisting predominantly of these.

Gridlock	Condition when congestion is so bad that it brings traffic to a standstill.
Hand-pitching	The practice of laying large stones tightly together on edge to form the foundation for a road.
Hardcore	Rubble from the demolition of concrete, brick or masonry.
Hard shoulder	Part of the verge designed to accommodate vehicles in the case of breakdown or emergency.
Highway	A main or principal road.
Hoggin	Naturally occurring mixture of flint gravel, sand and enough fines to act as a binder.
Hot-rolled asphalt	Dense, high quality, asphalt used mainly for surfacing on heavily trafficked roads.
Land take	The strip of land that has to be acquired for the construction of a road.
Lean concrete	Concrete having a low cement content.
Limestone	Rock consisting predominantly of calcium carbonate ($CaCO_3$).
Macadam	Graded crushed rock for roadmaking.
Mortar	A mixture of sand, cement or lime, and water.
Motorway	A limited-access, dual-carriageway road with grade separation, for the exclusive use of fast motor vehicles.
Pavement	The road structure above the subgrade.
Pervious macadam	Bitumen macadam with such a high content of air voids that it is pervious to water.

pF scale	The logarithm to the base ten of the suction in cm of water is the pF scale: e.g. 100 cm of water is pF 2.
Revetment	A protective covering to a soil or rock surface.
Road	A way for vehicles and other types of traffic.
Roadbase	The main structural layer of the pavement.
Roadmaking	The technical art of constructing a smooth, hard and durable road for the safe and economic passage of traffic.
Roadstone	Crushed rock or gravel suitable for roadmaking.
Rock	Massive, indurated, naturally occurring mineral material.
Sand	Rock or mineral particles 0.06–2 mm in size. A soil or deposit consisting predominantly of these.
Silt	Mineral particles 0.002–0.06 mm in size. A soil or deposit consisting predominantly of these.
Slag	Rock-like waste product of smelting iron or steel.
Soil	Soft or loose naturally occurring deposit resulting from the weathering or breakdown of rock or from the decay of vegetation.
Stone	Rock suitable for building or road construction.
Sub-base	The pavement layer between the roadbase and the subgrade.
Subgrade	The soil below formation level on which the pavement is constructed.
Subsoil	The firmer stratum of soil below the topsoil.

Suction	The stress-free negative pore water pressure of the water in the pores of the soil.
Surface dressing	A road surfacing made from a thin layer of chippings rolled into tar or bitumen freshly applied to the road surface.
Surfacing	The top layer of the pavement. Sometimes consists of a wearing course and a basecourse.
Tar	Black viscous material obtained as a by-product of the coal gas industry.
Tarmacadam	Coated macadam in which the binder is tar.
Thermistor	Electrical device used to measure temperature accurately.
Topsoil	The uppermost stratum of the soil containing plant roots decaying vegetation and humus as well as mineral matter.
Traffic	Vehicles, people or animals travelling on a road.
Turnpike road	A road on which a toll is charged to users.
Vehicle excise duty	Annual fee payable for licence to use a vehicle on the public roads.
Water table	The level of water in the ground.
Waterbound macadam (wetmix)	A roadbase material consisting of graded crushed rock pre-mixed with sufficient water for good compaction.
Weight	Force due to gravity acting on the mass of a body.

Useful Addresses

The libraries or information offices of the following organisations may be useful sources of information on modern roads and their construction.

British Aggregate Construction Materials Industries, 156 Buckingham Palace Road, London, SW1W 9TR.

British Cement Association, Century House, Telford Avenue, Crowthorne, Berks, RG45 6YS.

Concrete Society, 3 Eatongate, 112 Windsor Road, Slough, Berks, SL1 2JA.

Construction Industry Research and Information Association, 6 Storey's Gate, Westminster, London, SW1P 3AU.

Department of the Environment, Transport and the Regions, 2 Marsham Street, London, SW1P 3EB.

Institution of Civil Engineers, 1 Great George Street, Westminster, London, SW1P 3AA.

Institution of Highways and Transportation, 6 Endsleigh Street, London, WC1H 0DZ.

Science Museum, Exhibition Road, London, SW7 2DD.

Transport Research Laboratory, Old Wokingham Road, Crowthorne, Berks, RG45 6AU.

Index